*The Rules of Gravity*

# YOU CAN'T GET TO MARS WITHOUT ME!

MICHELLE M. TURNER

Published by FBRG, INC.

First Business Resource Group, Inc.
Phoenix, Arizona

Published by First Business Resource Group, Inc.
Phoenix, Arizona



President, First Business Resource Group, Inc.: Ken Jacobs
Layout and Graphic Design: Angela Payton

FIRST EDITION

ISBN 978-0-98329979-5-2

Printed in the United States of America.

10 9 8 7 6 5 4 3 2 1

*"In every walk with nature one receives far more than he seeks."*

- John Muir

*"With force, you get force. With rotation you get movement."*

- Michelle M. Turner

# Dedication

To my very special children, Gordon and Graham! They, without knowing the significance of the sum total of all their actions, unlocked a part of me that was hidden, needed to be developed, and is now able to offer a perspective in movement that has never been seen before. From this, I am able to learn from every child as I can now feel and manipulate gravity.

# Acknowledgements

I cannot go on without acknowledging Felipe Perez, Savithri Selvaraja, Dr. Medhini Singaraju and Dr. Kimberley Huggins, who are destined to hear every thought that comes out of my head. They have my back. Thanks also to Erin Fulks and Claudia Carmack, Betsaida Arrizon, and Amy Concillio whose constant questioning was needed to teach me how to explain movement. Thanks to Gordon, Amy, and Luis Lopez for your edits.

There are many people in my life at this very moment who offer a friendship and a bond. I thank them. However, I am at this very moment because of everyone who has said hello, everyone who has offered their time; I am grateful.

# Contents

**PART IV – Beings Interact With Gravity**



**PART V – What Happens When The System Fails Gravity**

# Foreward

I have been acquainted with Michelle and her work at Movement Lesson™ for some time, but it was not until I had the opportunity to work with her during the editing and publishing of this book that I truly realized the breadth and depth of her work and its impact.

Michelle is a patient and methodical studier and an assimilator of pertinent information that allows her to continually improve the work that she does, the impact that it has and the results that she is able to achieve with her clients. She is a consummate professional with much to teach. Her observations and resultant theories derive from thousands of hours of hands on practical work.

Read her book, learn from her, assimilate the information that she reveals, let your brain stretch to see where and how that new information applies in your area of expertise, and your life will never be the same. Enjoy the read!

*- Ken Jacobs*

# Prologue
## Biological Theories Of Gravity

**Gravity (noun)**

*Physics*

**The force that attracts a body toward the center of the earth, or toward any other physical body having mass.**

For centuries, definitions of gravity have been argued with interactions of mass, force, and light, yet there are still missing pieces around the organizing and understanding of our physical bodies, living beings and the universe within these principles. Over the past years, I have dedicated my life to helping my son develop basic life skills to sustain him as a human being. Suddenly finding oneself, after a profoundly traumatic, life-changing event the body must learn how to move in order to survive. The realization came to me that any cognitive and milestone achievements come from one's ability to move and organize movement. Practicing a gentle, functional touch versus applied muscle stimulation was key for any skill I was seeking. Over the past decade I have worked with over 25,000 children and adults.

I have developed movement techniques for special children of all ages. These techniques were developed as I discovered that the common denominator for all diagnoses and trauma is the lack of rotational movements. These problems create inabilities to respond to stimuli or to create transitional milestones.

In any living being, failure to produce and manipulate rotational movements not only guarantees that a child will develop with delays or special needs, it also guarantees that they will become an adult needing care. This combination of experiences is the primary reason for the body's rapid decline in outer space. The study of humans engaged in short and long-term space travel and colonization has included studies to the cellular level yet failed to discover the movements necessary to sustain functional movements defined in this book. Paradigm introductions of the needed structures of movement within biological gravity are contained in our developmental milestones. The architecture of our beings is not present in outer space and will impede us from getting to Mars. Contained in this book are the simple yet complex theories found in all bodies of life, from an atom, to the planets, and the spherical solar system. Within these organizations, we can find living examples of rotation resulting in the binding force called gravity. Simply put, people who don't have rotational movement can't move in and out of functional movements and will therefore organize to succumb to gravity.

All life forces require the ability to move within and oppose gravity. Within the first month of life, infants are exposed and are meant to develop crucial movements to organize cognitive neuro-responses as they synchronize within rotational and gravitational forces. This can be witnessed in natural childbirth, where the human body is first set up to experience this phenomenon from presenting out of the vaginal canal. This is a necessary experience to initiate the body's first rotation, muscle function transfer, and ability of neuro-mapping. This is therefore the first rotational milestone a human body ever experiences. However, when a newborn's body fails to experience or establish this relationship to the natural forces of opposing gravity through rotation and counterbalance, their brain is unable to create the necessary neural-synapses needed for development. Therefore, when a baby is unable to act on or is restricted from these natural and necessary movements, the biological laws of gravity are unable to establish its forces from within. We can look at any living being, whether on Earth or in outer space, prevented from responding to stimuli as they fail to oppose gravity with rotational movements, and we can see that they will immediately start succumbing to gravity. Why is this significant? When you and I are able to oppose gravity with rotational abilities, we can move in and out of all functional movements necessary for everyday skills and our inner life forces. The contrast is the opposite in all areas within these principles, as we will organize to succumb to gravity, unable to create milestones and with limited or no rotational movements whatsoever.

Through these movements, living beings develop in fluid dynamics, without opposing gravity, to create a being through the mode of expansion force. Oceans, tornados, hurricanes, and jet streams are all similarly created based on these principles. A living being's inner rotational fluid dynamics are as important as the movement structure needed to deliver and sustain the necessary force for their living gravity interaction. It is presumed that the primary reason for a living being's system breaking down in outer space is a lack of a gravitational force. However, a correct understanding of gravity does not support this presumption, nor is it how humans process the following principles for the abilities of living beings to thrive. Our response to and within this amazing biological gravitational phenomenon is an earth-based process and is caused when we fail to exhibit rotation as our bodies organize in succumbing to, not opposing, gravity.

However, gravity is not the only key to existence. Rotation is the necessary interaction for our brain's and body's ability to accomplish neuro-mapping. The first contributors to the body's failure in space are skeletal, muscle, and circulatory losses. These same losses occur wherever micro-gravitational locations impede our natural rotational responses. The natural resource of buoyancy is also needed in order to stabilize Earth-based movements. Because of that, a significant reason why gravity cannot be felt in outer space is the lack of oppositional rotational movements, and an inability to produce them. The natural result is an increase in our buoyancy responses. Consequently, humans are unable to produce earth-based milestones of standing, sitting, crawling, or lying down. During this time, an astronaut's buoyancy rates increase to dominate all movements, leaving them non-functional to neurological stimulation and therefore creating instant muscle neuropathy during their time in outer space.

I am newly defining gravity as the architecture of movement: gravity is the binding force of rotation fused with rotation. The oppositional, rotational movements attract from atomic rotation within rotation. However, true gravity is the core rotation binding to an opposition where living beings can sustain life as they interact with their own and complimentary internal rotational movements. Recognizing these key features in our movement structure in accordance with gravity as an introduction to the natural principles are needed for our understanding of gravity as a whole. Gravity acts as a rotational system that at the same moment binds us and creates the ability for the interaction of life as we know it. It is designed to establish actions needed with an internal reference to create an exterior action for life sustaining characteristics in our bodies, plants, planets and stars.

Adjusting our visual sense to acknowledge the force of gravity is not created by a wave; instead, it derives from two or more rotational forces interacting in opposition, creating a binding force. Natural forces include inner rotational movement, momentum, and buoyancy connecting, one force to another force. The prevailing understanding of gravity recognizes mass attracting mass, not location, as the key to the interaction of gravitational force; however, mass and buoyancy give gravitational fields the interaction to organize within the opposing force. Mass will always attract to a greater gravitational force in a perpendicular manner. However, within the same gravitational field, all organisms manipulate this same environment, without succumbing to a maximum force, for optimal life. The delicate play of opposing gravity is required in the birth of a plant from a seed to the start of our lives in natural delivery. Equally, and within a millisecond, in living beings, when the mass supersedes the might, the mass will prevail.

The criteria for a living movement structure can be identified as any object in space with functional inner rotational movement that supports molecular life. The establishment and interaction within the sciences of biological gravity is the key feature that attracts all living bodies to each other through rotational movements. Whether we are referring to atoms, our own bodies, Earth, the Sun, or the Solar System, rotational movements are the source of gravitational interaction between living organisms. Therefore, the Moon, having no internal rotational movements, presents with gravity arranged from centrifugal force and is thus unable to sustain living organisms. We get excited to witness the rare capture of a star's death. Assuming its gravitational force is so dense, it sucks the light and power from matter to collapse. In actuality, a star perishes due to lack of rotation, as the mass supersedes the might, destroying life as we know it. New dimensions in multi-planetary discussions can prevail as we recognize gravity's involvement with the formation and organization of the universe. Noting the framework within our existence, gravity is the skeletal system of the source of life, due to its structure and interaction.

Designed to live within gravity, humans format all cognitive and physical manipulations based on internal and external interactions through their body's ability to respond with and exhibit rotational movements. The more a living organism moves in opposition to gravity, the more it needs to increase its abilities of both rotational movement and buoyancy. These two forces regulate the responses of the body's internal processes to create locomotion in oppositional space. For us, space is complete and all around us with equal importance. We are capable of falling to the floor, yet at the very same moment we can climb, run, and/or jump with zest. For any and all movements needed for developmental milestones and life actions, i.e. functional movements, using rotational movement can make gravity's effect on the body appear weaker. Ease of movement initiates stamina and momentum as a force, not a required muscle-based action to be repeated. Opposition to gravity is not the lack of gravity; instead, it is the ability to use opposing movements within the bind of gravity, to create a force. It is these moments, interactions of forces and natural law, that are the dynamics of our evolution. Without our full understanding, our continuity is threatened, as we are unable to currently replicate these aspects of life on another surface.

Our brains are constantly acknowledging Newtonian principles, often offering images of an apple falling from a tree and astounding its receiver with a thump on the head. We don't seem to ponder what prompted that particular apple to relinquish its bond to that particular tree. Where in actuality, it is only when an apple's rotation and buoyancy fail to have an equal presence to gravity that the force of gravity becomes prevalent enough to create a superior binding force. Therefore, the apple does not simply fall from the tree, it succumbs to this overpowering force of nature. Forces remain a constant. They require no sudden or greater interaction to become dominant as the apple fails to leave the floor or change positions. In contrast, a living being will not just fall down like a board. It will have various responses to these forces through rotation and lack of rotation with factors of buoyancy that can counter the force of gravity as a part of the equation. Anywhere within its life continuum, when a person, or animal, is unable to regulate themselves within these natural forces, their structure of movement deteriorates, as they will not create typical vertical milestones with any equal momentum with gravitational force. A living being that is unable to create equal responses in passive and active muscle-based and force-based applications is the same as a person with no concerns for its relationship to life forces. Not only do new observations need to be made, standard and extreme calculations need to be made of non-rotational movements during this process due to lack of oppositional forces.

A healthy person does not start their day by prying their face off the floor. A dog can jump up onto all fours from the deepest sleep. This is due to our representation within the gravitational forces. We can mimic functional movements within this force, not against it. Until we assimilate and organize purposeful responses, our basis for all movement is a structure, not an action. For all living organisms, it is not about how gravity behaves, but how we act and interplay with the forces of gravity through responsive movements. Equally, living buoyancy and momentum must be at or within the same relationship with living rotational movement. The dynamics which are produced from these movements create our human subsenses. Our gravitational senses must organize to oppose gravity by interacting with it through play, not force; succumbing just as a baby entertains vertical challenges. Action senses must initiate with equal counterbalance before controlled attempts to balance come into play. Acquiring a sense of momentum through equal responses of rotation are necessary to respond to early stimuli before achieving and controlling acceleration. Early exposure to reactive senses of temperature and pain help bring in a perspective of self. Our kinesthetic senses start with proprioception and spatial orientation for orientation and mobility. Our initial five senses of touch, hearing, taste, smell, and sight are really stimuli receptors. Gravity is not necessary for our traditional or topical senses. How we organize within the biological features that gravity requires also requires an initiation and organization of our subsenses. This only occurs when movement intertwined with all of our senses creates early cognitive synapses for purposeful manipulation, which become measurable milestones and developmental achievements.

This book contains all the secrets of biological gravity. How it manifests through the binding force within each layer of our Earth's core through rotational structure to produce a force needed to integrate with the opposition rotational force of the adjacent core. This complex yet simple structure creates the same interaction needed for a flower as it rotates between the Earth and the Sun. A seed planted into the earth requires oppositional rotational movements, as its roots shoot for the core as the seedling births and immediately provides rotation for structured life. DNA, inner atomic and muscular structures, architects of beings, powered by movement dynamics, represents life and force as one. No longer can we view our feet pinned to the ground as we look to the stars from within the same space. The evolution of man and the universe will be based upon the ability to manipulate gravity in opposition. Space does not bend, but it represents the required receptive rotation within rotation to guide and interact for our presence in the solar system. Our futures depend on this knowledge being, not only shared, but utilized for our continued presence on Earth and into our future on Mars. Future studies will need to introduce the alterations of mathematical formulas of mass and acceleration to include our ability to manipulate space and how we move within that space. Changing play-based and working dynamics, the human body's system mechanics can only increase its developmental movement patterns in the manner that they have been exposed. The increased ease and manipulation by opposing the force of gravity to thrive can be witnessed with manual stimulation of rotation in equal and applied oppositional forces. We are at optical function opposing gravity, not overcoming it. Gravity is not located on the floor. The phenomenon is that mass cannot change direction or respond based on previous interactions. We are not mass, we are living organisms, therefore we need to rethink all views of performance in outer-space as non-muscle-based. Look at a tree growing towards the sky. Notice how it moves better the farther it gets from the ground. Viewing a body through biomechanics is a simple form of lift versus load. We measure the action of lifting a weight to produce an end result only because numbers are easier to track for progression of percent, not function. Weightlifting is a common ground for equal appearance but not for core movement integration. There is no cognitive interaction in a deadlift like there is in bailing hay or climbing.

As you enter into this book, I offer you new and exciting ideas responsible for all life as we know it. I challenge you to help in the needed changes for our future. I'll see you in space, but know that you can't get to Mars without the rules of gravity that are detailed in this book.

# Introduction

There are many aspects to movement that are based on the gravitational force. Movement, or the lack of movement, was introduced to me when my infant son severely regressed to a hypotonic, special needs baby. Frustrated with conventional approaches to help him with basic milestone achievement, I decided to take matters into my own hands, literally. I started with various programs that parents could attend to shed some light on how to help their special child. There was a lot of good information yet there were crucial puzzle pieces missing from the equation. Mainly the lack of basic evaluations to answer what would happen to my son and our family. My son had a massive and ongoing infection of Haemophilus Influenzae type b (HIB) and staph. It presented at 13 months and was undiagnosed for three years, despite over 20 surgeries and hospitalizations. His early years were concentrated on keeping him alive and making minor progress. His goal at 4 was to say 'Mom' and 'open'.

As I became engrossed with his progression, I quickly realized I was doing something different. I'm proud to say he started preschool at Foundation for Blind Child and progressed to self-contained Kindergarten. To date, he's the only child to leave special services (end of the third grade), he is a Black Belt, Life Rank in Boy Scouts, and proudly serves in his Student Council and Future Business Leader. As word got out regarding Graham's progress, I started to get noticed. When Johnjay, of Johnjay and Rich radio show, told me to start making videos I never looked back.

One night when Graham was eight years old, I was reading a book on Einstein to my sons. I was explaining the Space Shuttle as this majestic Rocket Ship rotating out into outer space. Three hours later, I jumped from my bed realizing all my clients, big or small, had the common issue of lack of rotational movements. This is why I was getting different and more efficient results, because my natural inclination was to touch with rotation. I've been studying aspects of movement and living beings ever since.

In 2016, I introduced the necessity for rotation and development. Stating if a baby is unable to respond to stimuli with rotational movements, they are at high risk for special needs. I wrote *The Newborn Movement Assessment™: The Evaluation and Stimulation of an Infant's*

*Developmental Movements.* The need to evaluate a child at birth to help them progress is a world-wide necessity.

In 2017, I presented my first theory of gravity, ***Turner's Theory of Opposition to Gravity and Locomotion*** at the International Movement Conference, at Oxford University, Oxford, England.

I also introduced concepts of movement and muscle responses in ***Perceptual Motion and Cognitive Development*** with Medhini Singaraju and ***Perpetual Motion in Human Beings: The Relationship of Movement and Acceleration in Locomotion*** - Oral Poster presentation ***Initiation and Stimulation of Functional Movement and System Mechanics*** with Dr. Kimberly N Huggins.

I continued with the Gravity Research Foundation essay competition, ***How Living Organisms are affected by Turner's Opposition to Gravity Theory.***

Neuroscience 2017, ***Making Neuroscience Accessible for Parents with Special Needs*** and ***Creating Volitional Movement with Cerebral Palsy*** with Kimberly N Huggins.

In 2018, International Movement Conference 2018 at Harvard University, School of Medicine, ***Infant Developmental Movement Patterns: Evaluation Techniques and Definitive Milestones*** and ***What is Standing? Redefining the Mechanics of Standing and Clinical Interventions*** by Kimberly N Huggins, Michelle M. Turner.

Most can be seen in ***What is Movement Lesson and How Can It Help You?*** https://www.movementlesson.academy

At this year's Gravity Research Foundation essay competition, I presented the foundations of this book with my ***Biological Laws of Gravity.***

I have proudly created Movement Lesson™ in my Peoria, Arizona clinic, travelled all over the United States, Bhutan, South Africa, Austria, Australia, England, Bahrain, India, Russia, and China. I teach others to be Movement Lesson™ Practitioners and help parents help their children, the ***Newborn Movement Assessment™, Cognitive Vision,*** going into my ***Cranial Series and Functional Anatomy*** and yes, ***You Can't Get to Mars Without Me.*** My podcast ***Movement 4.0 from Babies to Astronauts*** continues the principles found within these pages and my clinic in Phoenix, Arizona.

Twenty-five thousand Movement Lesson™ sessions later, I'm going to be explaining my findings based on the motion of force. I will refer to them as the "laws of gravity" to draw your brain to that which has already been presented by Newton, Einstein, and many others.

Just because I can drop a brick, ball, or myself at the same rate does not explain how our bodies initiate, stimulate, and enhance developmental movement patterns in relation to opposing gravity.

## Here is the gravity breakthrough:

My theories of oppositional biological gravitational and movement principles introduce human system mechanical requirements. This knowledge will allow a new conversation about long-term space travel that will promote the advancement of mankind in partnership with technology.

# PART I
# Perspectives on Gravity

# Chapter One
## Ticket to Mars

Since the thought of space travel first entered the brains of mankind, the search for a planet that would provide heat, water and oxygen has been a large priority to us. We shot the shortest distance and successfully landed on the moon. Since then, we've been floating around with countless biological experiments to measure the force and outcome of space-based living conditions. We have found reliable travel in space and on land with environmental units that are being put into position as this is being written. At the same time, 60 years after humanity's first attempts to reach outer space, we are no closer to having significant evidence of the human body's ability to withstand, much less thrive in, the short-term and long-term absence of gravity.

Many feel our evolution includes a multi-planetary existence by establishing a colony on Mars to get us acclimated to space. Our ability to endure and evolve are two of the necessary key points that will enable us to leave the third rock, planet Earth. One thing that we fail to realize, however, is that we don't have a true understanding of the essentials of how we move on Earth. Because these movements are functional for our survival they need to remain a constant within our system, wherever we travel to in outer space. More significantly, scientists have not yet grasped the importance of moving in space as if our bodies are still on earth. This book will introduce you to new dynamics on how we perceive, organize, and manipulate within gravity. The first challenge is to stop looking at gravity as an on/off mechanism or pinning force. Replacing traditional concepts with the acceptance that for all of our life forces and development we need to create functional movements in opposition to gravity. For a human being to create a developmental milestone or transitioning skill, they need to be able to initiate actions and move with the ability to respond to stimuli with rotational movements. This crucial and progressive structure of action is needed in simple living beings, as can be seen in the development of many species, from a pea plant, to human beings. When a baby is born without rotation or has limitations to move with it, the child is guaranteed to have special needs in both cognitive and neuro-muscular responses. This, in a nutshell, is what we are doing to astronauts. Mankind's lack of understanding of the simple, yet basic structure of movement, is why we, as a species, currently lack the ability or understanding to travel to Mars and beyond.

What do we currently know? The force of gravity can be recreated with acceleration for a G-force. However, gravitational force equivalent is nothing like how we experience gravity. The space program's approach to working with the human body goes against the body's natural approach for optimal neuro-mapping, cognitive formation, and physical structure. Understanding this, it becomes obvious that astronauts are unable to respond to stimuli because of their equal failure to produce rotational movements in opposition to gravity as soon as they are sent into outer space. In actuality, unless pinned or tethered to the space station, they are unable to respond with rotational movements of any nature. This is also one of the biggest misconceptions of gravity; that it is a force which brings us to another place. The Sun and Earth maintain a great relationship. The crucial dynamics of constant rotational relationships are apparent through the entire galaxy. This book will define all the secrets of gravity, which few have noticed, including simple, structural movements contained in every one of us, yet our astronauts lose them the second they leave our atmosphere. The sudden loss of movement's structure interacting with gravity's binding force brings an astronaut's body into anatomical failure within months.

Our continued reliance on Einstein's note of G-force application to space travel has done a disservice to the human body. He believed that if you suddenly woke up in a room with no windows traveling at one G-force of thrust application, you would not know whether you were on Earth or in outer space. It may potentially seem true in the first moments of awakening as it might be a true visual observation that not much has changed. Just look at basic space-based skills, not only are an astronauts feet not pinned to the floor, but they do not create a single movement using this technique. However, an observant person would quickly notice that their movements come from their feet rather than through their pelvis. You might also notice that they couldn't perform rotational movements. Or would you? Probably not. On Earth, however, this application of a body's ability to move is only apparent in a child or person with special needs in vertical manipulations. As adults we have assumed our origin and organization of movements are muscle-based, load/lift variations. Yet, when we observe a child, not only are they unable to perform, repeat, or master any skills, they cannot manipulate or control their muscles. A child has many abilities, yet they cannot teach or replicate simple to complex milestones. A variation of the pattern can be demonstrated but not an absolute. Adults are capable of these skills due to their capabilities to compare. As we continue to venture into space, the requirement for new movement processing needs to be taken into consideration on an individual basis.

Did you know that rotational movement is not taught in space rehabilitation, sports medicine, or conventional medicine and most early intervention therapies? Gravity is not just about how we use it, but also how we establish in, around, and with this binding force. This interaction is very different to what you learned in your science classes. It's time to learn a new way to experience gravity-based interactions, development, and evaluation.

## *The Background of Long-Term Space Travel*

Most of us can't remember an existence without the thought of mankind traveling to outer-space and beyond. The combination of travel and technological advances has made space travel seem more feasible by the day. Yet to date, long-term space travel is still inhibited due to concerns over human functionality in space. It is believed that prolonged periods of lack of gravity is the root cause of the physical changes to the human body. Although this is true, it's not for the reasons most people think. The stresses of outer space were immediately apparent to the Soviet Union and the United States starting in 1961. The first cosmonauts and astronauts were dizzy and had issues walking immediately upon their arrival back to Earth. The feeling of weightlessness in outer space was somewhat unfamiliar compared to Earth's conditions. While he was in space, Yuri Alekseyevich Gagarin, Russian Soviet pilot and cosmonaut noted: "Here, you feel as if you were hanging in a horizontal position in straps. You feel as if you are suspended."

Before we even knew we could get to outer space, there were already programs and applications dedicated to the study of the effects of short- and long-term space travel and the maintenance of human functions during the travel.

Over the past 60 years, we've put plants, animals, and humans into space, with technological advancements helping to increase flight times. Unfortunately, an astronaut's body changes after their return to Earth and may include many mild to severe life-changing effects to their body's structure and functions. A consistent result of space travel is that astronauts return with enlarged hearts and bone deterioration at the top of their list of issues. All human muscles atrophy, which include the elongation of the spine, and these processes are only worsened when put through the trials that come from space travel. These physical and mental changes lead to long-term rehabilitation programs for the astronauts to help reestablish them to Earth's presence. "Right after I landed, I could feel the weight of my lips and tongue...I hadn't realized that I had learned to talk with a weightless tongue," reported Col. Chris Hadfield, Canadian Astronaut.

Many in-depth studies are conducted in various locations here on earth, in various altitudes, and even on the Mir space station. Projects have included the Twins Study, where scientists compared now retired astronaut Scott Kelly's body, DNA, organs while he was in space to his identical twin brother, now retired astronaut Mark Kelly, who remained on Earth. Projects such as these have allowed studies from basic muscle function to the endocrine system and genetics. However, all of the studies to date fail to represent core movement integration before, during, and after for all body processes. Changes are needed in our chase for outer space for effectiveness, transportation of equipment, and the necessary ability to adapt to these programs during long-term space travel. This is where the direction of space travel has faulted with various attempts to allow man to help mankind.

The biggest failure of short-term and long-term space travel is the lack of understanding of how the body develops in relation to the neurological response of man's relationship to Earth's gravity. We need to adjust our thinking to include the required biological gravitational responses in order to create the programs necessary to enable astronauts to travel in space for long durations. Instead, we keep doing the same thing over and over again, while expecting different changes in human dynamics. For almost a century we have known that this is the definition of insanity. The answers to these challenges are not in the places that science has looked so far. Isn't it time that we took a fresh look at the principles of gravity and our relationship to them?

Every day, I witness what happens to the body when these forces have not been established or are traumatized when gravity becomes a pinning force. The lack of or inability to respond to gravity creates an abnormal force response that some bodies cannot and will never adjust to. This is true because they cannot initiate a movement foreign to their biological structure. However, when you present functional movement and key principles of rotational responses within opposition to gravity, a severely delayed child or adult can suddenly or over time start to produce movements previously thought to be impossible. Realizing the same inabilities are presented as daily activities by our astronauts was, to say the least, life changing. By the end of this book, you will understand how our bodies base all cognitive and body functions on their ability to oppose gravity, not to simply respond to it. It's within these two forces that a human sustains any and all neuro-typical functions. Our physical interactions include responses through the muscular, skeletal, systematic, cellular and movement systems. Movement is structured through these two opposing forces that stimulate and maintain balance, counterbalance, momentum and acceleration. Current muscle-based and range of motion evaluation techniques are primitive, outdated, and erroneously inaccurate. They are used to satisfy visual observation needs which present no benefits for astronauts or those with special needs.

NASA has also recognized that the problems that occur during space travel are due to the lack of balance and sense of direction. These views have been further directed to the increased volume of fluid in the inner ear. Although it is true that the body will have impaired balance when the inner ear is traumatized, this is not where the sense of balance is formed in the developmental movement patterns or milestones of the human body. The sense of balance and counterbalance is one of the first developmental milestones that an infant has experience with as they respond to stimuli. In all human actions, the body's system mechanics oppose and submit to gravity in equal and opposite forces, creating balance and counterbalance. Humans do not stand pinned to Earth's gravitational force for their feet to propel a person upright. Previous assessment of standing considers only linear movement and that standing is driven from the feet and ankles up. "Astronauts experience bone loss, muscle loss, cardiovascular deconditioning, and more in space." Torin K. Clark, Assistant Professor of Aerospace Engineering Sciences at the Ann & H.J. Smead Department of Aerospace Engineering Sciences, University of Colorado, Boulder said: "Today, there are a series of piecemeal countermeasures to overcome these issues, but artificial gravity is great because it can overcome all of them at once."[1] Science fails to realize that artificial gravity won't solve a functional movement deficiency issue. Lack of proper functional movement is the reason we are seeing physical failure in humans, from babies to astronauts. The human body only organizes through functional movement in opposition to gravity in combination with rotational responses.

Movement is more complex as it involves integrating a full sphere of inputs from around the system to create the necessary opposition to

1 Artificial Gravity Breaks Free From Science Fiction, July 2, 2019 ScienceBlog.com

gravity, as well as the counterbalance and drive rotation that is the underpinning of movement. The act or movement of standing is achieved when the system mechanics acknowledge the force of action into the floor and at the same time, the upper body opposes that equal and same action to rise above the feet. Core movement opposition engages through the pelvis to initiate the action, but it is not a muscular function. This is a key factor that needs to be understood in order for mankind to continue it's conquest of space. Continuing with the belief that a solution will come from artificial gravity, no amount of money, time, or equipment will aid mankind in their desired outcome of sustaining longer life in space.

With the determination to succeed added to the advancements of computers, aerospace technologies, and the introduction of commercial practices, the exploration of space holds the potential of turning into general space travel within our lifetime. Collaborations between governments and corporations such as SpaceX, Orbital Sciences, Blue Origin, Bigelow Aerospace, Dynetics, Astrobiotic Technology, Virgin Galactic, and iSpace have created realistic plans that could launch us to Mars in the near future. Now more than ever, we need to not only sustain astronauts, but create a healthy environment for individuals who are less than physically fit.

It is believed that there are mild to substantial changes that occur in human physiology in a non- to low-gravity environment. It's true that due to the lack of pressure directing the actions and flow of fluids, there are many cases of apparent visual abnormalities that include swelling in the face, neck, and surface veins. This is thought to be true due to the astronaut living without gravity. However, science has been viewing these and other human functions from the wrong point of view. The common belief is that we are able to exist on Earth due to gravity and if it weren't for that, we would all float off the earth. If it weren't for gravity, the sun would explode. If it weren't for gravity, the apple wouldn't fall from the tree. The core purpose of this book is to teach how gravity truly affects the human body as a system, where functional movements are created within. Without understanding the concepts detailed here it is impossible to make any substantial progress regarding human space travel.

Let's begin looking at what really happens when humans are in outer space. As soon as the rocket leaves our atmosphere, at the split second of the introduction of a G-force thrust, the binding force, or interaction through rotational movements able to be produced by the human body, ceases to exist. At this very moment, every movement that we have accomplished and created effective synapses for cognitive neuro-mapping are no longer valid in our body's form. At this point we lack the ability to implement developmental and functional movements to thrive without gravity. During this interaction, the body may respond to or mimic static or linear movements, but none of the new movements created are functional. Therefore, our brain will no longer fire or activate muscular, skeletal, or system responses that were needed a minute before.

An adult body functions as it does due to its foundational first movements that provided abilities to accumulate through weight transfer and transitional movements. Initial movements during the neonatal period, our first months of life, are only able to respond to gravitational responses. The first rotational milestone that the human body ever experiences is during the process of a vaginal delivery. In natural childbirth, the human body is set up to experience this phenomenon of presenting out of the vaginal canal, a crucial experience to initiate the body's first rotation, muscle function transfer, and synchronized neuro-mapping. However, when this doesn't establish or is prevented, a baby's body fails to experience the natural forces of gravity and establish rotation and counterbalance to counteract its effects. These missed movements are considered early intervention risks of short-term and long-term developmental delays and may be a guarantee that they will occur. The experiences of astronauts in space are similar, because when they leave the experience of gravitational force interaction, they no longer have the abilities of rotation, muscle function transfer, or synchronized neurological responses. An astronaut immediately loses the ability to perform all developmental milestones. Outer space provides an environment where mankind can no longer stand, walk, run, crawl, transition between sitting to standing, roll over, or lie down. If a child or an adult on Earth has issues and inabilities to respond to these stimuli, they will immediately start to succumb to gravity. This is primarily due to the lack of the ability to oppose gravity with rotational movements. This is an earth-based process and when a body fails in its ability to create rotation, the brain and nervous system organize in succumbing to gravity, not opposing. In space, since there is no gravity or rotation, the body's buoyancy rate increases to dominate and succumbs to changes. Due to the decrease in gravity and the inability to interact with the Earth's binding force, the brain's nervous system cannot counter the momentum. Along with this, most human sub-senses are no longer present in our bodies due to the lack of our inner responses that include rotational movements. Balance, counterbalance, responses to gravity (opposition and succumbing), rotation, acceleration, proprioception, and spatial orientation immediately leave the system. Some of the confusion is currently addressed through exterior stimuli responses but not as a system-based experience. An astronaut's inability to create or produce functional movements misdirects their principle approach to exercise and continues to cause problems with space rehabilitation and information regarding muscle responses for strength and stamina.

To think we only have five senses is certainly not going to get humanity to Mars. Just because someone can taste doesn't mean that they can balance. As the weight of the apple hits our hand, immediate inner encounters arise to bring the fruit to our mouth. Balance and counterbalance are called into action through the skeletal system as the hyoid interacts and gauges the tongue's interaction and draw of the teeth. None of these minute movements can happen in outer space. An astronaut may think it is novel to suddenly suck their food out of the air and catch it in their mouth, having sensory input to the palate rather than the tongue. This is the first of many major crashes to their nervous system and they never see it coming. Why do you think a dog teeths on a toy, pulling and snarling for hours in delight? Why do you think that a baby puts everything into their mouth? These push/pull interactions to our vertical milestones give us our power to perform. Astronauts didn't think to create exercises for the mouth and head movements, which could explain why their faces start to bulge.

A crucial observation is the realization that under current conditions, not only can humans not 'stand' in space, their bodies also cannot produce any major developmental milestones. With the inability to oppose two forces, a human cannot come to sitting, crawl, run, or skip, and the human nervous system equally finds difficulties and regressions when responding with mature psychological functions, such as in sleep, social skills and anger moderation. What actually presents is a type of space 'autism.' Their inability to play well with others is viewed to be a complication of micro-living conditions. Instead, evaluation techniques need to be established for how each astronaut organizes and produces movements prior to and during space time. New processes need to be implemented acknowledging that emotions are developed and then respond with movements.

Although it is true that without gravity we would float away and not exist, we must also realize that all neuro-pathways, cognitive impressions and developmental movement patterns are based on optimal, opposition of gravity. For any and all life forces to oppose gravity, the act of rotation must be present in all initial to mature movements in the body. By re-evaluating developmental movement patterns in babies during their early stages, I have witnessed that for any system to respond to stimuli and create a cognitive response, the infant must exhibit rotation. This is one of the key gravitational laws that must be recognized and applied to prevent or reduce the failings of the human body during space travel.

Another key aspect to prolonged existence in space is recognizing that a human is unable to produce functional rotational movements without assistance. On earth, it is known that, unassisted, it is impossible to restart any organ function in the human body. If a person's heart fails, for example, they better have someone nearby that can restart it, otherwise the situation can become very bad very quick. The same is true for rotation. When a body does not present or has traumatized abilities to produce rotation in opposition to gravity, it is necessary for a trained professional to initiate, stimulate, and enhance those movements in the body. This can be done through a hands-on approach or specific equipment.

It is widely believed that the key to human function is based on muscle function. It is also widely believed that since there is little need for muscle function in space, the muscles quickly atrophy. However, muscles do not create a movement; they respond to movement. Just because someone can contract a muscle in their bicep does not mean that they can feed themself. Therefore, if an astronaut reorganizes all of their biological formations to not need their muscles to respond to functional movement, they begin to deteriorate. It's that simple. This is why professionals who, despite having dual PhDs and working out for four hours a day, still have immediate physical deterioration as they enter space. This happens because of our irrational relationship to muscles and the idea that the human system can produce movements based on muscle function as long as the might supersedes the mass. Space exaggerates this relationship: where there is hardly any might for an action, the cognitive nervous system becomes equally complex. All space-based tasks are created through organization and problem solving. Although this is needed for life management the complications of functioning to action/interaction changes our inner dynamics. When this relationship is reversed the body can't move or the astronaut needs to regain strength upon his arrival to Earth. Immediate changes are needed in our program of exercising the body in long-term space to include functional movement patterns based on the opposition to gravity and two opposing forces. When these new clinical movements are typical to the human that is performing the functions, the brain responds in a more typical manner, therefore increasing its ability to sustain a life with less change.

This holds especially true with the sudden increase to bone mass causing a premature osteoporosis. It's the pull of muscle on the bone while in the opposition of gravity state that strengthens bones. This constant pull of the bone maintains and/or creates density depending on the environment. On Earth, as soon as a person hangs off of their skeletal system or shortens their gait with a forward and/or downward manner, the muscles now hang off the bone. Therefore, not only are they not maintaining bone strength, it is the quickest form of aging as the organs also hang from the system. The introduction of movements that create the function of pull against the bone during each session of exercise should decrease the global effects of bone loss. The introduction of the principles of movement which include my Biological Theories of Gravity are crucial changes needed to proceed into space. Fear that astronauts will be unable to endure prolonged space travel due to weakness and skeletal breaks are a core breakdown in the space program. The factors that are clear in establishing human development cannot be overlooked in a mature adult system. The conversations are not the same for a human system that remains on Earth. However, that system cannot be kept in the same regard when you are removing all cognitive responses that the body has learned to respond to, to grow from, and to trust.

# Chapter Two

## What You Don't Know About Gravity

Science tells us that we really don't know where gravity comes from, or for that matter, where it is going. It is presented as a perpendicular, pinning force that attaches matter in a downward position or a fall. At the same time, we don't organize to fall down nor do we fall straight down. Gravity is currently viewed as a wave traveling through the universe, yet it seems to be consistent in a building or in a cave. Water and amniotic fluid change the force of gravity without pulling us to the bottom, so it's constant yet quite weak. So weak, as Marcus Clown mentions in The Ascent of Gravity: The Quest to Understand the Force that Explains Everything, you can raise your arm against gravity with very little effort.

I was doing research when I realized that my discoveries through Movement Lesson™ were not available to the public. Gravity is still elusive, and although it is the greatest gift of all of nature, it is understanding how we organize to gravity on Earth and within the solar system that is critical.

Crucial biological gravitational responses for living organisms are needed for us to sustain life. Just because you supply water and sunlight to a seed doesn't mean it will grow or bear fruit. Most avenues of science don't understand movement within gravity. We celebrate and admire the approaches, the changes, and the advancement in the space program and the technology that intertwines with short-term and long-term space travel. However, the drawbacks include taking the same approach to improving the human form that has remained static over the past half century. This approach is based on a barbaric idealism of believing in a perfect form capable of achieving great feats, yet it only surrounds high performers and ignores the body's basic, creative functions. While the space program has advanced over the past half century, in 2020 we still maintain this idealism, forgetting that these basic functions are rendered impossible in zero-gravity environments. No amount of physical perfection on earth makes any difference in space.

Again, understanding and implementing my theories of oppositional biological gravitational and movement principles, thereby introducing the human system mechanic requirements, will not only allow a new conversation to occur about long-term space travel, it will also promote the advancement of mankind in partnership with technology.

**What is gravity?**

I am presenting the following observations to organize and represent the nature of gravity.

1. Gravitational force is created not by a wave, but when two or more rotational forces interact in opposition, creating a binding force.
2. Biological gravity is a binding force structured to attract all living bodies to each other through rotational movements.
3. Gravity is involved with the formation and organization of the universe. The organization and existence of gravity is due to rotational movements. Any object in space with functional inner rotational movement supports molecular life. Therefore, objects that do not have an inner core with oppositional, rotational movements do not support life.
4. Within gravitational force living beings can mimic any movements within this natural force, not against it.

**What is gravity in relation to all movements presented by living beings?**

5. The definition of opposition to gravity is not lack of gravity. It is the ability to use opposing movements within the bind of gravity that create a counter force.
6. It is this inner rotational movement, momentum, and buoyancy that binds one force to another force.
7. It is thought that mass, not location, is the key to the interaction of gravitational force; however, mass and buoyancy give the gravitational fields the interaction to organize within the opposing force. In living beings, the interaction with gravity as a whole, organizes func-

tional movement and neurological synapses through the equal combination of buoyancy, fluid, and essential rotational movements.

8. The basis for all movement is a structure, not an action. For all living organisms, it is not about how gravity behaves, but how we act and interplay with the forces of gravity through responsive movements.
9. Rotational movements are the source of gravitational interaction between living organisms.
10. Humans organize all cognitive and physical manipulations based on internal and external interactions through the body's ability to respond with and exhibit rotational movements.
11. The more abilities are increased in both rotational movements and buoyancy, the more a living organism can move in opposition to gravity. The two regulate the response of the internal processes to create locomotion in oppositional space.
12. For any and all functional actions, using rotational movement can make gravity appear weaker.
13. Gravity is not felt in outer space because there are no oppositional rotational movements. The binding force of gravity within living beings can only interact through internal rotational movements; otherwise one is more dominant than the other.
14. A living being's inner rotational fluid dynamics are as important as their movement structure to deliver and sustain the force needed for their living gravity interaction.
15. Living buoyancy must be at or within the same relationship with living rotational movement.
16. Living beings develop in fluid dynamics without opposing gravity to create a being through the mode of expansion force. There are no rotational movements during this process. There are no oppositional forces during this time. Other than during fetal development, when gravity and rotation cannot be felt or organized, living organisms that lack rotational movement and exposure to oppositional forces start to fail as an internal structure, developmentally and anatomically.
17. A living organism will not just fall down like a board, but will instead have variations of the response through rotation and lack of rotation with factors of buoyancy that can counter the force of gravity in living beings. Equally, a living being, when traumatized or prevented from establishing a relationship to gravity, will experience the retreat of natural oppositional actions, and succumb to these forces.

**When does gravity fail? Perhaps a better question is; when do we fail in relationship to gravity?**

A living being, when traumatized or prevented from establishing a relationship to gravity, will experience the retreat of natural oppositional actions and succumb to these forces.

18. In living beings, when the mass supersedes the might, the mass will prevail.
19. Any living being unable to regulate themselves within the binding gravitational force will not create typical vertical milestones without initiation, stimulation, enhancement, and the ability to breathe in equal momentum with gravitational force.
20. A living being that is unable to create equal responses in passive and active muscle-based and force-based applications, is the same as a person with no concern for its relationship to life forces.
21. A living being manipulates the lower binding force of gravity to catapult movement from above and thereby creates inner momentum. On the contrary, inanimate objects may become a pendulum interacting with both the Earth's gravity and rotation in isolated momentum as a constant.

Grasping and utilizing these principles of biological gravity is immediately needed to help people with special needs, from babies to astronauts, because these same principles of natural law are in everyone. Since mankind has done nothing to change any of our architecture of movement to sustain life other than on Earth, *You Can't Get to Mars Without Me.*

Let's look at essential deviations, in muscle-based interactions, that are not possible in outer-space. They are the reason for immediate atrophy and cellular decline. In both categories, it is imperative to halt the discrepancies and possible breakdown of the human body in order to ensure the future success of humanity's efforts in space.

The possibilities for all mankind depend on you reading, understanding, and implementing the contents of this book. If we don't change the course of the number of special children being produced, we will bankrupt our government and community-based programs and support. If we don't change the course of our training for space travel, we will continue to produce astronauts with needs that we have no effective means to treat. We are ready for the shift needed to help the way our bodies grow and become cognitively fluent.

Yes, we have concrete signs we are ready for complex, multi-planetary experiences, but what you don't know about gravity...could kill you!

# Chapter Three

# Everything Falls

One of the prominent laws of gravity comes from Sir. Isaac Newton having a life changing altercation with an apple. Since then, we have always been told that everything falls. But does it really? Viewing gravity as a pinning force, as experienced when any mass is destabilized, and will fall to the floor. And yes, if you or I were to fall, we will fall down; but we don't organize around the ground. Why does gravity bring us down? Why can we go years without a fall? Why can't some people ever walk? Does a tree really fall down? When a living being is drawn to the floor, it can be due to falling but it can also be due to lack of ability to oppose gravity.

Let's look at this from another point of view. An astronaut has been in outer space for a few months. Landing in Kazakhstan is rough as the crew is greeted by men who need to carry out each person, as they are unable to walk and can barely move. Why does this happen? Because they need to re-learn to oppose gravity through rotational movements. The same scenario can be presented through the eyes of children with special needs. Due to genetics and/or birth trauma, their first rotational movement was limited or was unable to initiate. Immediately, their systems will start to oppose gravity. This realization changed my entire approach to movement: astronauts move with the same infrastructure as special needs children.

As an astronaut is learning to walk again, we concentrate on the basis of muscle atrophy, yet a little old lady can get to the market without core strength. You can quickly view videos of the returned astronauts and clearly see the lack of rotational movements. Also, you can clearly see five people around them, so they won't fall down. When was the last time you had people around you to protect you? While you were intoxicated? Or immediately after surgery? The same can be found with small children. You create a safe environment, so they don't wander into a dangerous situation with the stairs. However; with a special child, you cannot let go because they will fall.

What if I told you that we don't fall down? There is not one thing that you are doing currently where the thought of falling is present. If you are, not only are you not going to be able to get to Mars, you'll also need someone else's assistance for you to accomplish your daily tasks. The organization of not needing to fall has nothing to do with strength, age, or gravity. Or does it? If your nervous system cannot make a movement without calculating whether you might fall or be unsuccessful at what you are about to do, your body is now formulating movements with the binding force of succumbing to gravity, or simply put, going or falling down. In other words, if your nervous system is focused on not falling while performing a task then your body is now formulating movements in relation to succumbing to gravity rather than moving through it. Falling down could be a dangerous, fearful, or neurological calculation. If a tiger were approaching, you might need to run and not fall down in the process. You might need to cross a slick surface to get to the car. In those circumstances, those thoughts are good. However, for others, you may not want to go on a hike with friends because you might fall and hurt yourself. Another person might not want to leave their house or even their bed because they might fall and break their hip. Those thoughts might seem practical, but they are not. The human body should not be in a situation where the prevention of a fear-based fall is the primary forethought. If a person startles and spasms in a lying or seated position, neurologically, their entire nervous system is based on succumbing to gravity.

My first memories of my son's recovery from his regression is that he would constantly fall like a drunk. In his attempts to maintain walking were his attempts to not fall down. He could go sideways, backwards, all top heavy with a hard fall, only to get up again. I was told he was low tone, hypotonic, and until he got stronger, he would continue to fall down. This was when I started to question movement. Why was he falling down and a child next to him wasn't? Watching children at the park or pre-school, I would see that this baby wasn't falling down, yet, this other child, possibly with cerebral palsy was in a full defense to not fall down. From these accumulations of observations, I have created a modality around my principles. Every hour I see a client that was given a diagnosis that comes with unanswered questions and no way of evaluating short to long-term care or goals. It became very evident to me why and how their relationship was not interacting to gravity, not responding to the 'gravitational binding force'.

You see, I work with and help people whose bodies are afraid, only know to, and/or are preventing the action of falling down. When you have a senior who has just fallen, they will have excuses as to why it happened, but many times, it will simply happen without much prior context.

If you don't catch the crucial organizational shift from opposing gravity to succumbing to gravity, the body and brain can quickly fail. This is one of the main reasons as to why most people pass on within a year of breaking a hip. It's not a medical or muscle-based response, but instead a system-based response. Any person who is unable to respond with rotational movements is now organizing or neuro-mapping to succumb to gravity, making it difficult to leave their internal and external reference to the floor.

As humans, we don't organize our bodies to fall. In actuality, we learn to fall down when we are infants. A typical baby is only capable of responding through weight transfer. During this stage, falling is not an option (unless manifested through an accident). It's a very precise form of interaction within our structure of movement. In toddlers, you need to fall to be successful in vertical interactions. One significant point of a toddler grabbing their feet and crawling is learning to fall. What goes up, must come down. For those who ski, how to fall down is the first lesson that is taught. Einstein's theories state that the Earth is falling or pulling away from us with enough power to bring us to the Earth. In space, the fall is greater because our bodies are perpetually interacting with a space fall. However, I wish to make note that our bodies don't recognize or interact with that sensation unless we are special needs or we actually lose our footing.

I agree that we fall at the same rate as the apple. Why does an apple fall from a tree? It is when its relationship to inner and outer rotational movements within its buoyancy ratio change or diminish and the mass is now greater for gravity to be dominant. This is a key observation when viewing how living biology responds to or interacts with gravity.

Let's take a moment to recap and take a new look at gravity based on our revised ideas presented so far. We can now see that gravity is a force that attracts all bodies. The way to see how this force binds us together is through rotational movements. When rotational movements are unable to organize in opposition to gravity, then the same interaction, more commonly referred to today as a force, pulls us to the ground through a technique known as falling. Furthermore, a body that is unable to organize in opposition to gravity with rotational movements is now organizing to succumb to gravity.

Gravity is a difficult subject when it is viewed as coming from an outside source or a wave. Gravity is also viewed as a force pushing you down. The dreaded step on the scale, calculating your weight can be a perfect example of the force of gravity. Yet a block of gold and lead will offer us different weights, despite being the same size. When you and I both throw a ball, how, when and where will the ball reach the basket? Do we measure the mass and distance or the person's range of motion? Clearly, we can measure and calculate an apple, bowling ball, or light falling to the Earth. Let's start reviewing and discussing how we interact with gravity as a living being.

# PART II
# What is Gravity?

# Chapter Four

# Gravity-The Force From Within

## *Turner's 1st theory of biological gravity*

**Gravitational force is not created by a wave, but when two or more rotational forces interact in opposition, creating a binding force.**

> *"Imagine occupying a windowless chest in outer space, a container that was being accelerated at a uniform rate by some propulsion device. At a certain sustained rate of acceleration, it would become impossible for the occupant to tell whether he was stationary on Earth or gaining speed in a distant void, for all physical operations inside the chest would be identical."*
>
> – Einstein's thoughts on gravity

Each layer of Earth's core moves in opposing directions. Within these opposing layers are the secret movements needed to create momentum, or a binding force, as the draw of the intertwining actions causes the natural force to be a constant. A stronger bind rotation contained in a star is the stellar convection zone where the current is circular for a stronger binding force. This phenomenon is a stunning structure of movement needed for life on and in a planet, but also for how we live, organize, and survive. This illustration continues; as a bigger picture, each planet has opposing rotation interacting with the others in various spherical motions that bind its solar system. Each solar system is spherical. Any planet, any atom, in any system, has an inner rotational core to create molecular activity, which may be something that you and I might call water, oxygen, atmosphere, etc.

Reflecting on a representation of a wave, it is just a linear representation of a rotational movement. It would be impossible for a human being to respond to a wave as an anatomical function: therefore, it is impossible for gravity to be a wave. How could it be possible? First of all, humans and living beings are organisms that operate from movement created from within. We are not designed for exterior movements. Second, if gravity was a wave, we would be sensitive to different Earth experiences of increased and diminished gravity depending whether we were on mountains, in caves, or in our homes and offices. While gravity can cause a wave, it can't be a wave. Inconsistencies would show from rubber bands left around a newspaper to the simple, yet complex aging process. They would be subject to ranges of movement deviations hour to hour and day to day. Plants, animals, and human beings are far too sensitive to have different gravitational pattern responses. We clearly see this in outer-space, days of leaving the flexibilities of gravitational interaction rather than deviations. The breakdown of our anatomical architecture is due to the lack of rotational movements in opposition to gravity, not purely the lack of gravity as an entity.

Rotational movement is the structure in atoms, DNA, myosin/actin (interior structure of muscles), functional movements, jet streams, planetary motion, solar system and beyond. Let's go back and look at interior movements. The same can be said about planets and suns. Living beings are structured to create or produce functional movements from the inside. We are not made to produce a movement from an external force. Therefore, to assume there is a wave of gravity approaching any beings or going through or around any of our systems does not create or sustain a living interaction. It is our inner relationship to rotational structure and elliptical sensation that is equally enhanced by the Earth, the Sun, within the solar system and the gravitational binding force found around us. A common solar burst would interrupt wave formation. Gravity, defined as a wave, also suggests a frequency or power, requiring a constant of force and response. Here's a simple example: a dead lifter would have a different gravitational response than a teenager learning piano. Caves and structures would vary our neurological and muscle-based responses as if gravity was trying to push us over or prevent an action.

Here is an easy example of the binding force of biological gravity I have discovered and use in my practice. If you were to spin around, having optimal rotational and functional movements, as a more or less typical human being, you come into yourself or spin inwards. Likewise, if your system was impaired, due to drugs or trauma, attempting a spinning motion, needed for the necessary binding force, $\infty f$ you would go away from yourself or spin outwards and fall down. Taking this further, when a healthy body spins around with a healthy baby, the infant automatically clings to them. However, a compromised infant will not bind and will fall away from the person spinning with them. The difference or lack of inner rotational movements is evident from the first hours of birth. Viewed as a simple exercise, it can also be profoundly powerful as a diagnostic tool, identifying babies at high risk for short-term and long-term developmental concerns.

An atom is spinning as the nucleus opposes an electron, binding the unit together. Blood cells rotate as part of your circulatory system. The recognition of a body's ability to tap into the source of perpetual motion is not only enjoyable but can be developed into higher functions of skill and achievement. This presentation of inter-rotation within the skeletal muscles creates an implosion of perpetual motion that will create a new spin on function and propulsion of the human form. Biology teaches us that skeletal muscles include muscle fibers that contain several nuclei that wait for a signal from the central nervous system to contract or relax. It is within this coordination or alignment that you can now see the internal force of perpetual motion in locomotion. The similarities of nature's version of an internal combustion engine show the actin and myosin filaments/fibers creating the stored kinetic energy needed for propulsion. In the sliding filament theory of muscular contraction, it is believed that when a muscle is relaxed, tropomyosin blocks the cross-bridge binding sites on actin. The sliding filament action of muscle contraction is actually the mechanism of movement that contains an energy source for opposing the two forces creating momentum, movement, acceleration and cognitive manipulation. The creation of a pull onto the muscle fiber produces and stores the energy that is needed for the action. The release of this action allows the release of energy into the system mechanics for a controlled reaction and/or action. Another significance of this new function is to view the health of the muscle fibers in relation to the rest of the body's system mechanics. As a muscle releases from contraction, the myosin reverses their opposing spin with the actin. This allows the muscle fiber to not only lengthen but to aid in the movement of fluids. As we change this view of anatomic function to functional anatomy, we can view the actin and myosin of the muscle fiber moving in a rotational spine to create a kinetic energy for perpetual motion.

# POP QUIZ:

**Question #1: Are the changes in rotational jet streams within our water and atmospheric systems affecting inner core rotation and mantle displacement? Calculate the changes for environmental comparisons with Mars.**

## *SPACE-BASED COMPLICATIONS*

While in outer space, an astronaut is able to move through the space station in a free-floating manner. However, this is only what it looks like to the naked eye. A free float is impossible due to the restricted space within the International Space Station (ISS); therefore, many movements need to be anchored with a push/pull organization from the hands and the feet. There are lips all around for an astronaut to hook their feet from the top. All movement as they know it is now altered. Any developmental movement pattern is rendered useless and the body quickly alters muscle organization. There is no evidence of this necessary movement going through their body maintaining any functions. Presented in this book are new opportunities to explore our relationship to biological gravity and its critical role in structuring our existence.

Muscles play a major role in performing day to day activities and in infants the ability of the muscle to respond to stimuli is key to the development of the cognitive skills. Skeletal muscles as well as the involuntary muscles can be manipulated to become automatic, or deliberate cognitive responses, depending on the human's stage in relation to their developmental movement patterns.

## *SPACE-BASED ADAPTATIONS*

If the Big Bang did not create rotational movements, we would not have a universe. We wouldn't be here to recognize time or reality. Therefore, we can also study the formations of new solar systems and their rotational movements to calculate and determine the ability to form a planet. It is the collection of these internal movements that creates everything from atoms to solar systems.

In adults, the formed cognitive response to stimuli is processed in a filing system in the brain and the desire to initiate new movements into the system mechanics typically diminishes with age. Adults will have also formed opinions and potential outcomes of how most movements are to be performed by them and by those around them. When a developed brain is challenged to a new learning opportunity, it will predetermine a pattern or group of steps that need to be achieved for this new process to occur. In addition, the brain will establish a time limit for lack of achievement within one or more of the proposed goals. The standards for continued development of the matured brain cannot be mirrored in an infant or child. It is also within these differences that perpetual movement, momentum, acceleration and cognitive manipulation begin to stagnate and/or diminish. In the adult mind, the cognitive process will base many decisions for growth and development on past performance and character development rather than with a playful sense of wonder.

Movement is the key to all functions of life as we know it. Stimulating functional movement and rotation within the human body rather than associating strength with accomplished lifting actions can improve the cognitive processing dynamics. Additional research is needed to show the interplay of muscle function and cognitive function in developmental milestone achievements. Creating specific exercises based upon these principles is crucial for reversing the aging process and creating optimal movement patterns ranging from those with special considerations to high-end performers.

# PART III
# How We Organize to Gravity

# Chapter Five

# Movement Within Gravity

## *Turner's 2nd theory of biological gravity*

**Biological gravity is a binding force structured to attract all living bodies to each other through rotational movements.**

> *"Gravity explains the motions of the planets, but it cannot explain who sets the planets in motion."*
>
> – Newton's thoughts on gravity

Since Newton's time, discoveries have been made that all objects are attracted to one another through a gravitational force. However, since that time, we have been fixated on force and falling. A seemingly simple structure of a perpendicular manner that pulls an object to the ground. We can agree there is a force or attraction between two bodies, and many things can fall down. However, the falling down isn't the true action of gravity. Gravity is a binding force structured to attract and interact with other living beings and mass.

Let's look at all living beings, the Earth, Sun, the Moon, and the Solar System. The most overlooked quality of movement in the abilities or inabilities of these bodies is interior and exterior rotation. This simple, yet dynamic action, is the binding force of the universe because it creates living gravity. Living gravity is the natural force or byproduct of active rotational integration in opposition to gravity as a whole. You see, all living organisms create functional movement in opposition to gravity with rotational movements. At the same time, we can examine gravity to be involved with our organization of oppositional rotational movements to create the dynamics of "living gravity". An object, with lack of rotational movements and buoyancy will always succumb to the byproduct or constant of gravity, when in close proximity to a living rotational generator, or core. Biological gravity interacts with the forces created in oppositional rotational movements as found in everything from atoms to layers of the atmosphere.

Living organisms need rotational movement in opposition to gravity to thrive and survive. Yes, we are talking about atoms, our bodies, planets and plants. The Sun doesn't breathe or produce life as we know it, yet the molecule exchanges needed for its continuance are the same. Grasping this concept allows us to understand why when rotational movements are unable to present, organized in opposition to gravity, this interaction - or what is known as force - pulls us to the ground through a technique known as falling. A body that is not in the status of falling, is functioning in opposition to gravity. A body that is unable to respond to actions in opposition to gravity with rotational movements is now formulating to succumb to gravity.

The key observation in this theory is not only the obvious rotational movements, it's the inner rotation that is needed for life. A simple observation can be found as we compare the Earth to the Moon. The Earth, containing layers of inner rotation, presents with gravity and with life. The Moon on the other hand, having no inner rotation, does not support life. These observations can be seen on Earth and throughout all our galaxies. I would like to note that my definition of life is the interaction of moving molecules. You can flush a toilet bowl and see how sensitive a molecule is to rotation. At the same time, you can observe that the motion of rotation is also a binding force, not a pull or secure platform.

The Earth's core to atmosphere ratio is substantial: inner core to the ionosphere, outer core to the exosphere, d-layer to the thermosphere, lower mantle to the mesosphere, the upper mantle to the stratosphere, the asthenosphere to the troposphere and lithosphere, the continental crust to the oceanic crust. Since the Moon's core is twenty percent of the size of the Moon, having no atmosphere renders a no-show to oppositional movement with any rotation. The Moon's core is only twenty percent of its mass with an inner core, outer core, partial melt, mantle. The Moon therefore has no rotation, is tidal locked and produces centrifugal force. Therefore, the Moon does not have an interior or exterior rotation, produces no oppositional gravity and is unable to present with life.

Since our first experiences with the Moon, scientists have experienced an uneven or bumpy orbit and gravitational pull on its surface. The Moon's surface gravity is about 1/6th as powerful as what we are accustomed to in our movement organization, or about 1.6 meters per second per second. However, there are impact craters that experience a higher gravitational field. This is another example of why gravity can't be a response to an exterior wave. One theory of why the Moon's surface gravity is weaker is due to its smaller size compared to the Earth. Limited research has concentrated on the Moon having a lack of various layers of inner cores. In addition to having no axis rotation, the Moon's movements present through centrifugal force, not a gravitational binding force. This is why we never see the far side of the moon, as if I were to swing a bucket of water not losing a drop; this type of rotation will not bear or sustain life.

Using the same evaluation, Mars has one-half the radius of the planet Earth. Mars is a small planet almost equal to the size of the Earth's core. It has very little core to atmosphere dynamics to include a core to the exosphere, a mantle to the mesosphere, and a crust to the troposphere. It is further from the sun, but it also has a revolution period 686.98 per calendar year. Not only do we need to look at the inner to outer oppositional dynamics but the actual spin for the type of gravity a living organism needs to sustain it.

It is the oppositional rotation that holds the key to gravity as we know it. The first and most obvious calculations need to be gleaned from the Earth's core. Each section of the core is and needs to be rotating in opposing directions. There are many aspects of weight and density but key to our relationship and need for Earth is the binding force. Newton looks at a force as matched in opposition. When we have a rotation within a rotation, the opposition creates a bind or a type of pull. This is not to be confused with centrifugal force because that is a pinning force, as seen on the Moon. A pinning force versus a pulling force is a different interaction for us to perform any and all things with. We need the ability to perform tasks with rotational movements. This is why the Moon presents with no life or is unable to sustain life. Therefore, this force, or living on the Moon, would eventually kill us. We'll be covering more of this complication within another gravitational law. Living beings have to live within the boundaries of the needed binding force of gravity for evolution and performance.

Another example, if you have ever played with a hand gyroscope, this force is very apparent. First of all, if my hand and body do not offer the equipment a rotational interaction, it will not respond with movement. For every action there is an equal and opposite reaction: with rotation, you should get counter rotation. As the shell moves between your hand and the gyroscope, you get a binding force that is unlike a true gyroscope that creates percussion and centrifugal force. Your hand creates a greater force as the object increases its spin efficiency. This is a very simple example of how gravity works. The earth's inner and opposition rotational movements are creating a biological gravity. Not only is it interacting with us, but with the solar system and universe.

We can reverse this principle as we take a look at the death of a massive star, otherwise known as gravitational collapse. Science tends to, once again, view the falling or condensing of the space as increasing the core's density. Where in actuality, its lack of rotation is the first observation. In this case, if the core were to maintain its inner and outer core rotational movements, the star cannot collapse. We need a new mathematical discipline that can systematically document the binding forces of gravity, which prevents the collapse or fall of an organism; the true structure of the universe. This would be true for the cluster of bodies, as seen in galaxies and stellar groups. Discovery calculations can also be used to find these units in the universe's creation.

It is agreed we need gravity to sustain life as we know it. It also needs to be noted this type of gravity is the structure needed for our body to produce functional movement and create neurological pathways. From a baby being born, a child skipping, a tree growing in the woods, these living dynamics are all based on the opposition of gravity. The production of gravity happens when the rotation within rotation is specific enough for a structured binding force. The rotations within rotations continue with moons orbiting planets, which therefore orbit suns, which rotate into a solar system. The dynamic variations in binding forces, which are the necessary calculations for life, are seen in a molecular exchange. It is true, humans and living beings on Earth, require the addition of air and water. Jupiter or the Sun are very much alive within their specific offering of gravity. Our ability to calculate and recognize the specific type of rotational gravity can be used to examine the oppositional movements needed and then adjust to the type of life to be sustained and reproduced somewhere other than on Earth.

# POP QUIZ:

**Question #2: What is the oppositional force needed to produce a rotational movement for function? Calculate the rotation within the rotation of the Earth's core for the global binding force emitted for gravitational life.**

## *SPACE-BASED COMPLICATIONS*

The very first concern is that humans and living beings cannot produce a rotational movement while living in outer-space. We have been told that the only missing piece to space travel is gravity. In its lack, muscles atrophy and the circulatory system is compromised due to the lack of pull to the human body. However, it is not the lack of gravity causing complications to human tissues, but the absence of movements needed to oppose gravity. This is the missing link to man's ability to endure long-term space travel. Based on current training, when we have no gravity or are unable to oppose gravity, the body lacks the capability to produce the rotational responses needed for all functional movements. Equally, the decrease in rotation and gravity and an increase of the body's buoyancy rate dynamics. This drastic increase is too great and causes an astronaut to float. These same principles are the key factors that influenced how I determined a different way to work with a special needs child's body and cognitive skills. The common denominator for any diagnosis, is traumatized or lack of rotational responses to stimuli. How do I know? This is my first theory! What does an astronaut have in common with a child with cerebral palsy? They are unable to produce a functional movement in opposition to gravity due to the lack of or inability to respond with the needed rotation. The mathematical failures that are produced within oppositional movements are noted in both acceleration and deceleration to the action needed. The action alone is static and for most is unable to be reproduced - no different than two pitchers throwing out a ball over home plate in the same conditions. The speed and action of the ball might have similarities, yet the production of the movement differs from each human based on how they identify and manipulate gravity.

Earth-based actions of these forces can be created in station tasks to replace current modules, as with MARES or treadmill endurance, cardiovascular and other endurance experiments. These are not and do not include any developmental movement patterns needed for a single functional movement. The very second we leave Earth's last atmosphere, we also lose the opposing force needed for walking and sleeping. Any and every task needed as a cognitive and body-based life skill, is unable to be produced. The action of eating is capable, as a tube is squeezed and caught into the astronaut's mouth, but this is a pure example of an action, not a force or skill. During this period, adaptations of functional movements within simple to complex oppositional gyroscopic equipment needs to be reviewed and implemented for short and long-term durations.

You do not! I repeat, DO NOT want to replace human beings' organization to a gravitational binding force with centrifugal force. Conversations include the manipulation of a spinning space station or a colony on the Moon. We need to note these are not artificial gravity but another structure of movement which has no approach to our life force organization. Why, you ask? Because it's the complete opposite of what I am presenting here. It's not gravity and it will destroy the brain and the body. There are a few sports that you can do that produce centrifugal force. Surfing, skiing, skateboarding, are on the list. Catching a rotational wave while pinning our feet through this force can be very addicting to some. Notice that you are placing an inanimate moving object under the feet through a pulling force, not a binding force. When the brain switches over to the pulling force, something neurologically happens. The person finds it very difficult living in the 'real' world. They become very antisocial and seek the sensation to be pulled rather than holding a job or relationship. Not only would it be very expensive to add rotation to the space station, once the astronaut's system switches over to the new force, which will be almost immediate without the counter of an oppositional force, the person on the other end will be answering the mike with 'Dude, what's up? How's it hanging?" Also, it will be even more difficult to rehabilitate the astronaut back to a rotational binding force. Therefore, you would have complications assimilating the person to a Mars based community.

I will also go out on a limb and predict that the human being or plant will start to die. As mentioned, functional movement is a movement that goes through major and minor organs. The heart and lungs will have immediate difficulties in their interaction. Just because one of the complications is floating internal fluid dynamics at a cellular level, doesn't mean that you want to pull those internal functions towards the ankles. First of all, there are no organs past the pelvis. Limbs are for action-based, not survival- based movements. The structure of movement interaction is needed for active and passive responses to stimuli. Just as we lose all of our developmental milestones in outer space, except for standing and lying down, centrifugal force will produce the same consequences. The key missing element is the ability to respond with rotation in opposition to gravity.

## *SPACE-BASED ADAPTATIONS*

There are plenty of ways to change all of space travel to include these principles. Redefining functional movements as the primary source of 'exercise' on the space stations and colonies. There needs to be a daily system and neurological interaction of a body in expansion mode and one that is in opposition to gravity with rotation in a 360-degree response environment. Hard core aspects of oppositional training can be produced to cover all areas of not only muscles but organ and bone with circulatory and lymphatic aspects of movement momentum.

Conditions of reinstating and reconstructing all or most of the infant developmental movement patterns need to be addressed. This must include gravity-based reflex responses needed for continued skeletal articulation, in and out of daily living for bone articulation and long-term emotional consequences to reduce the neurological changes which may create space-based autism. Similar to doing our chores, specific activity-based movements with momentum also need to be studied. Tug-of -War or push-pull games can convert two systems from one-on-one interactions. Synchronized group movements may be added into plant and animal studies. We need to adjust to recognizing the source of a particular gravity and its binding and rotational influence to core dynamics to produce the life force needed for our living bodies. All Earth organisms format movements based on the interaction of both the movements and in opposition to gravity while interacting and organizing with all twenty-one theories presented herein. Evaluation and assessment techniques need to be developed and implemented for our evolution.

# Chapter Six

## All Around You

### *Turner's 3rd theory of biological gravity*

**Gravity is involved with the formation and organization of the universe. The organization and existence of gravity is due to rotational movements. Any object in space with functional inner rotational movement supports molecular life. Therefore, objects that do not have an inner core with oppositional, rotational movements do not support life.**

> *"It's gravity that shapes the large-scale structure of the universe, even though it is the weakest of four categories of forces."*
>
> – Stephen Hawking

We have been pondering about the beginnings and the formation of the Universe ever since we have noticed the stars above. From the planets and the stars, a notion of gravity came into play and our wheels have been spinning. This is where we need to redirect our focus, from the art of falling to rotational binding. In the formation and function of every living planet, star, and solar system is a collection of inner rotational movements. Oppositional rotation creates a binding force needed for all life as we know it. There is not one form of life able to begin without this simple mathematical formation. Particles are in a particular set of rotational movements. These are the essence of a solar system. Mass gravitates towards the center for star formation, then this process happens again to form the planets within. Just as not all force is equal, not all gravitational force is equal. Each planet has a different size as well as different inner cores organizing at different rotations, speeds and axis points. They also have different moon rotations that may or may not influence their inner core rotation. Each planet has a different relationship to the sun. Have you ever thought about how our planet's rotation influences the sun?

You see, we were taught that the solar system was a static disc where nine planets orbited the Sun (I'm including Pluto because it was a planet when I was taught this). It was to my surprise when I later learned that we are actually chasing the sun. The sun is visually before us, pulling her little planets behind her. Or we can also take the point of view that, similar to magnetic coils, the planetary rotations are propelling the sun through space as the binding force keeps us within these dynamic movements. Adding force to the conversation, if there is another planet in our solar system, Planet 9 would be in the outer reaches in oppositional rotational orbit.

The apple that falls from the tree is the apple that is dying. Arranging thoughts based on movements can go beyond interacting with gravity to look at the source. The introduction of rotation creating the opposition of gravity also needs to be looked at from the source. Let us break away from the famous apple falling to the Earth for a bit to examine the fall or the bind. The binding force is more practical to the outcome of the action. Viewing the initiation of the action reveals more than looking at the results. At the same time, let us look at the source of rotation. Rotation and bind are equally important in this equation. The force or action of the fall is thought to be the act of gravity. An apple falling to the Earth is an act of gravity, not the creation of gravity. Or is it? Within the Earth we have eleven cores. This includes conversations of rotational surface actions but does not include atmospheric levels. Each core rotates in opposite directions and is thought to be because of different weights of each core or magnetisms. Both thoughts are equally important for discussion and, like the apple, it might have a great deal to do with gravity. In contrast to assuming that the centripetal acceleration of the earth is the main source for the gravitational force, we must notice how each core rotates around the other core, creating a binding force that goes beyond Newton's Law of Motion. When a surface rotates around another surface as a whole, it creates a stable but strong force that is gravity.

There is a force that generates and that cannot be diminished unless the rotation slows or ceases to exist. The other cores work in tandem to stabilize, enhance and perpetuate this force beyond the earth's surface. Sub-rotations are continued through these conversations of inner-planetary movement as they continue through the elements of nature. These demonstrations of the Coriolis force are all wonderful exhibits of motion relative to a rotation reference frame. Moving beyond the clockwise and counterclockwise reference to action and counteraction, through rotation, equally forces the object's deflection. The two most notable instances can be seen in flushing a toilet on each hemisphere creating oppositions in rotational response to nature, with the other being hurricane or storm rotation magnitude with environmental coordination. Storms, wind patterns, tornadoes are continued rotations that all dance within this equation.

Let's take a moment to discuss that there is a noted biological difference of a binding gravitational force to that of a centrifugal force, as seen in the moon. What is centrifugal force? Imagine going to the carnival or amusement park and feel the force of the Tilt-O-Whirl or a roller coaster. You may want to lift your hands above your head and keep them there, but it's very hard to do so. This is the sensation of centrifugal force. Weight transfer and rotation cease to exist as we enter into might over matter. Just as if I were to spin a bucket of water with a certain momentum over my head, the water will not succumb to gravity and I will never see the bottom of the bucket. This force is the reason why you and I will never see the far side of the moon from the Earth. This is why the moon is no more than a giant rock that is attached to the Earth in a seemingly fixed orbit and why it does not have life, nor will it be able to biologically support a human being for many reasons. As we have discussed before, gravity is overlapping as a constant force from rotations.

Currently the term Coriolis effect or referenced with Earth's rotation is only viewed on the surface. French engineer and mathematician, Gaspard-Gustave de Coriolis demonstrated the rotations on a frame of oppositional force at right angles, not as a binding force of a rotation within a rotation. Examples of living organisms being perpendicular to the rotation axis and velocity of Earth's rotation offer a countermovement to its actions, but in small forces that are not equal to that of the planet. These forces are also noted in directional travel using the poles of the Northern and Southern Hemisphere for momentum and deflection, which can be seen with atmospheric events and wind direction with the division of the equator.

Stars that have a large mass with their own inner core rotation are able to operate as the center of their own solar system. When there is enough collection of mass, that starts a specific rotation to create a star. At the same time, a star that cannot hold or display the moment of inner and outer rotation will collapse. Within the nineteen observations currently being studied for galaxy formation, the star's rotation is as equally important as the mass that is rotating around the new star's formation.

Our solar system is based around our sun. The mass and rotation are of equal importance, as both created the opportunity for Earth development and for ecosystems to form for living organisms. The space between the Sun and the Earth must also be noted. Each planet within our solar system has a rotational spin with inner cores. When this rotation is not noted, there is no atmosphere, or if there is, it is unsuitable to support life. Our moon has no rotation; it operates solely off of centrifugal force. We will never see the dark side of the moon from our planet's surface. It is a spherical rock that moves around us in orbit. There are certain moons, however, such as Titan and Europa, that must have the kind of rotation quality discussed earlier in this book. The planets not only have a specific orbit around the sun, they also have a specific rotation. The solar system is also moving through space, creating an additional rotation around the rotation of our solar orbit, further creating a binding gravitational force. Every galaxy similarly exhibits a rotational binding force.

Similarly, the human body is not organized for exterior movements. Neither are the planets, stars, or solar systems. However, all observations of accomplishments are valued by exterior performances. The confusion comes from how we were poorly taught how planets orbit around our wonderful Sun. Some may think that we orbit the sun in a nice round orbit. That's not entirely true. We may still use the word orbit, due to our connection to the sun, planets and moons spherical relationships, however, we are not in a fixed 'orbit'.

In our solar system, each planet and moon have an orbit. Looking at this illustration, we are all in an interlocking dance similar to a strand of DNA (Another example of how many aspects of life are related to rotation!). Due to these interactions, there are clever planetary escape velocities, meaning that we need to adjust to the planets' inner core rotation to the exterior rotation for moving in and out through its atmosphere

It is also thought that because the Earth is not a perfect sphere, it wobbles as it tries to rotate on its axis. They are noted rotational facts, but we are still able to organize within those movements. You cannot look at a ball on a string and call it a planet, as it lacks layers of inner and outer rotational movements that we interact with. One of the reasons it is so difficult to climb Mt. Everest is due to lack of atmospheric pressure. In actuality, it is the severe decrease of our body's interaction with rotational movements. Similar to an incapacitated system, walking as we know it is no longer a stride with the ability to counter at a cellular level, but a load/lift variation as we now pull our feet from a surface as Newton's third law kicks in. This is no different from rocket propulsion in escape velocity.

A few years ago, my boys and I very excitedly saw the movie, 'Hidden Figures' in the theater. Even as I write this, it's not a history lesson of who did this and that. The same concept has propelled me in this work because most of the people I work with are not in any book. Their anatomy can be very different. Their bodies respond to movement and structure in seemingly unimaginable ways at times. I have chosen not to pursue a formal education in anatomy and bioscience because most of the modern thoughts that are presented are theory and are not based on functional movement. As I'm not one for facts, enjoying the specific details contained in a history I wasn't a part of, I'm more interested in watching a rocket take off. I would whisper to my son, 'It's not going to make it. It has no rotation," as it proceeded to explode. "This one is a good one. It has rotation." And the rocket went up.

Inter-planetary exploration, especially to other solar systems, will require a complete study of inner-planetary to solar rotation calculations in order for habitation to be possible.

# POP QUIZ:

**Question #3: What is the binding force of each planets' core in relation to their rotation, speed, and axis in regard to opposing the direction of other planets and the sun?**

## *SPACE-BASED COMPLICATIONS*

There are different forces required to land on the moon's surface in different locations. However, we cannot calculate the force of the moon as gravity in regard to living beings. Science tells us it does have gravity because it has mass. It does attract us to the surface, but it does so in a different manner. We clearly remember the interaction of buoyancy and reduced gravity with non-rotational movements, seeing the astronauts on the moon bounce around, hop and fall down. The first time they fell, they continued their movements as a continued series of events with the attempt to not fall.

It should be noted that individualism is not a desired aspect in a space setting. However, the additional movement complications of centrifugal force will first change the social dynamics to one of force and power. As seen in similar movement situations, from surfers, skiers, and skateboarders, to name a few, the addictiveness and adrenaline rush surpasses reason. The brain rewires for this new stimulation of thrill and adventure dominating the social will. Their physical system remains healthy and strong, until the first major fall. Then the nervous system recalculates movements to prevent the falling. The inner conflict begins, seen as aging, or inabilities.

If we feel compelled to set up a lunar colony it is imperative that we establish an ecosystem that mimics gravity, not centrifugal force, or it will not support our form of life. Spinning an adaptable ecosystem crosses two aspects of centrifugal force. Apparatuses will need to be made so that astronauts are able to spend more time in oppositional force to include neurological and system-based rotational movements. Otherwise, their bodies will fail at quicker rates than exhibited in the space station. Either example offers the body a tether-based interaction with movement. The space station has a higher rate of expansion mode. The moon's surface has a greater experience with gravity but creates projectile movement responses, increasing force and momentum dynamics into the astronaut's nervous system.

## *SPACE-BASED ADAPTATIONS*

On the moon, exercise equipment needs to have the foundation to include all of the developmental movement patterns. We need the ability to maintain transitional milestones, not just static images of standing. The key to human dynamics is the ability to go in and out of a situation. When do you panic? When you don't have a solution to a problem. When does the body panic? When it has one or no movements to respond with. It is in the comparison of movement-based interactions that cognitive developmental responses are established. When people come to my office, they have a direct solution to get there. If there is an accident or flooding, our brains look for an alternative to the task for efficiency. This is a simple example, yet it is key to our neuro-mapping establishment. Functional movement creates the body's responses to our environment. This must be established in space-based protocols, not only in standard exercises, but in living environments.

Fatigue in humans, observed by volume of speed, strength, and time, happens when mass supersedes the might. In general words, fatigue is a body's inability to move mass by any and all means of force. It is unable to perform mundane to intricate tasks. This mass does not need to be an external force, weight, or act that needs to be carried out by the use of moving an external object or counterweight. It is actually the being that succumbs to gravity in a resting state, frailty, or death.

Human beings in high performance categories play with this equation in gymnastics and swimming, to name a few. However, this constant and inaccurate manipulation of mass rather than movement leads to the demise of health and the inability to compete at that constant and static level.

The new gains in opposition to gravity will not only change the mathematical formulas of mass and acceleration, but will also increase man's ability to manipulate space and how he moves within that space. The amount that humans will be able to change their internal and external awareness of the space within gravity will expand their cognitive and functional core to new levels of exploration not seen to date.

# Chapter Seven
# Going Around in Circles

## *Turner's 4th theory of biological gravity*

**Within gravitational force living beings can mimic any movements within this natural force, not against it.**

> *"The Universe is circles within circles, and everything is one circle, and all the circles are connected to each other. Each family is a circle, and those family circles connect together and make a community, and the community makes its circle where it lives on the Earth. It (the community) cares for that part (of the Earth) but cares for it as a circle - which is to say in a cooperative and egalitarian way, where everybody is cared for, and everybody is respected."*
>
> – Black Elk

In our lifetime, we've delighted in the forces of nature by spinning a bucket of water over our head; to our amazement, the water magically stayed in the bucket. At first you assume the pulling force is gravity, alas your science teacher tells you it is affected by gravity but is continuing in a straight line as gravity is still trying to pull things down. At the same time, the water's inertia wants to keep the water on a straight path, against the force of gravity, offering a generated force or the illusion of centrifugal force. It's the centripetal force keeping the water in the bucket. It is when the various motions change momentum that we risk the falling water. A significant observation to assimilate is that the body of water is not moving. Observing movement through an inertial frame of reference, mass can move around the center yet a living being has no axis point because it is not linear, therefore there is no rotational movement, weight transfer, or centrifugal force - only centripetal and inertial forces. This is one of the key reasons we cannot create any of these forces in space and refer to them as artificial gravity. How a living being organizes in opposition to gravity is just as compelling as a force preventing movement. They both have a significant impact on life.

A dominant reason we are looking at action within actions, is that this creates mimicking and repetition. For the increase of muscle mass, man has started to organize routines and movements that mimic one successful movement. This misconception of repetition is similar to inertia on the human body as an exterior action producing an interior response of only stability. A person bends over and does butterfly lifts with twenty-pound weights to initiate responses for muscle mass and maintenance. Isolated repetitions against the supposed forces of gravity is the success formula for optimal health. There is one problem with this thought process: just because someone is strong does not mean they are able to move. For a human being to represent functional movements they must be done within the force of gravity.

The organization of living beings has life-force dynamics within the gravitational forces equal to our structures of movements. In living beings, gravity is not a pulling or pinning force. When we interact with gravity, unless we have special needs, we never feel as if we are being pulled or pinned to the ground. Part of the definition of movement is "in opposition to gravity," therefore we need to have rotational movements. It's this configuration for any and all functional movements to happen. A serviceable movement or developmental milestone is a method of mobility for our personal survival. A tomato plant needs to rise up at its oppositional, rotational structure to survive and bear fruit and seed. A typical plant will stay within its range of height, width, age, and product yield. Until now, you would consider sunlight, earth, and water as the basis for life. We are looking at the organization of the plant's progress until it perishes. The architecture of movement needed for functional movement is equal to the relationship to gravity. A baby, having trauma at birth and respiratory distress, will be unable or at high risk for all issues in development due to the fact that it is unable to organize within gravity as needed. The inability to represent within gravity is equal to the failure to mimic movements that are functional.

The Vitruvian Man shows man's interaction of proportional movement. It suggests, however, that the origin of human interactions stems from adult configurations. From the Fibonacci spiral numbers or nautilus shell, (the Golden Mean) to circles within circles, we can develop and analyze static movements with exterior direction and define man through visual assessments of prone and supine, flection and inflection. Worse yet is to approach human movements with integration of these static arrangements with little or no long-term gains. Range of movements are based on measurable outcomes for abilities that are just measurements.

They do not include transitional movements or the ability of maintaining structure in opposition going from one position to another. In optimal situations, a person's social, emotional and physical combines with a level of intelligence that is deemed necessary for them to become an astronaut, athlete, or a person that is admired through their country or field. Once home from space, astronauts are not able to move because the buoyancy and cellular interaction has changed, and so has the movement of mucus that interrupts the vestibular system. The cognitive neuro-mapping of rotational, transitional movements are interacting with the mucosal movements necessary for weight transfer and milestone development. The critical necessities of buoyancy have a hierarchy beginning at the skeletal, visual, lymphatic, respiratory and then cellular level. This is the first interaction to leave the human body in outer space. The lack of a visual horizon for balance and space-based interaction causes some of the first problems.

Primitive man was stronger because there was no room for weakness. Man procreated with the knowledge that many offspring would not survive, nor would there be a long life to those that are unable to provide for their purpose to the tribe. The modern consciousness that primitive man existed in weak conditions is also what gave that same species strength that is not found in today's man. There are little or no thoughts of this type of existence in what is to be considered modern man. Another note with affluence, there are little or no movements that humans perform where their arms rise above the shoulders. The lack of need to hunt, climb, farm, prune trees and hang laundry have all but disappeared in society functions. Without thought, those tasks are left to lower and/or uneducated classes or equipment.

The concept that the first thought of natural survival is size has been noted within the species. Today's man varies in height from five feet to a high six feet. What was once considered small and agile are clouded by higher considerations of height and even natural appearances offering additional signs of health and virility. Winston Churchill was born two months premature and grew to be a great leader despite his ability to show strength. He noted many predators that gave him a cognitive strength to prevail despite many hardships, not to him, but to his people, that he was a known protector. Is he also an example of a domesticated animal that can prevail, not because of inner species survival but because its fellow man will not allow harm and provides an artificial nourishment that includes a controlled environment and the possibilities of medical aid for critical and preventative care? It is likely that we can answer that question with a yes since he was Prime Minister into his eighties and served during several noted strokes.

When you are sick with the flu, it's not that you can't drive a car due to the symptoms of the illness; the inflammation, viscosity and slowness of the mucus changes the body's system dynamics into succumbing to gravity. Therefore, a sick person's body is unable to process certain movement skills. Simple, mundane tasks of spatial awareness or balance are suddenly debilitating, not because the person is unable to know the movement, it is because their interaction of inner movements is impaired. The internal heaviness of the system is too much for cognitive responses to overcome and/or they overcompensate balance and spatial judgement. We can analyze the same movements or neurological processing as the same for astronauts. Since an astronaut's body is attempting to float, the neurological responses are immediately organizing in counter opposition. Mucus does the same thing in outer space. Seen as a nuisance, however, this phenomenon begins immediate changes within all the body's dynamics.

## *SPACE-BASED COMPLICATIONS*

A rocket needing to escape Earth's atmosphere also needs to have enough thrust to oppose gravity. To do so, the rocket needs a rotational momentum that coordinates with the Earth's rotational movements. From the calculations, we now have to put a human being in the rocket to get them where they need to go. At first, an astronaut is tested to withstand the force of the rocket. The propelling of humans to outer space not only creates a pinning force but disorientation, nausea and possible black out. It is during this time an astronaut is unable to mimic or create functional movement. During this period, the pulling of G-force is not gravity yet science refers to it as such. Where does this approach to gravity fail us with similar observations?

When mass moves, we have measured this phenomenon as a type of force per unit of mass. The most common way is through rate of acceleration. Noting again the apple falling to the ground, we can easily calculate the size, distance and rate of travel or applied force. However, as you are learning, we don't organize to fall or fail. Gravity doesn't pull us to the earth. We might fall to earth, but we are not pulled to earth. During no time during our personal evolution are we pulled to earth. Nor are we organizing movements in order not to fall. Artificial gravity creates a force that initiates those movements. From there we can start to see the demise of gravitational force equivalent versus the needed force for our consistent movement for cognitive and body awareness.

Currently there are no artificial representations for artificial gravity which is needed for torque presentation. More importantly, each astronaut needs to be evaluated for their mass distribution and stress in mathematical coordination for personal rotational ratios needed to take priority versus standard body mass index (BMI), range of motion, strength and stamina. Expecting astronauts to respond to a G-force, these principles can be expanded for the most efficient response. If you were to hit, I would naturally want to hit back. This is a primal experience of force to force response. This is not the way a body creates movement, only how it responds with applied force.

## *SPACE-BASED ADAPTATIONS*

Understanding gravity as a structure of movements is a new and necessary concept as we send astronauts and colonies into space and onto planets. Many forces of momentum, including G, inertial, centrifugal and centripetal forces do occur. They need to be recognized as a force, but they are not and cannot represent or replace gravity. It's the spin that binds us to the earth so we can function independently. It is our inner rotational movements that are needed to produce complementing and counteracting neurological gravity-based responses produced from the Earth's interaction and its atmosphere.

It is within these dynamics that a human being is able to represent most movements in concert with true gravitational forces. We cannot do the same or equal creation or imitation of any movements through artificial, micro, or non-gravity environments. Space-based applications of routine and daily exercise in astronauts require specific applications addressing their personal mass differential and rotational ratio. Any personal positioning based on a pull dynamic needs to be removed from the space program and replaced with these new specifications. The International Space Station is a microgravity environment. Any and all activities aboard the Station need to be systematically altered to add rotational movements to those activities. Exercises and strength-based movements need to include all of our developmental milestones. Some of the key reasons for the Moon's inability to hold or produce any life are the Moon's inability to produce core/atmosphere binding forces to interact with and the Moon does not have a barycenter organization of the Sun but to the Earth. This is a shorter distance with a tidal lock. Any lunar colonization needs to be seriously evaluated and arranged for the survival of our lives. Living on the Moon without changing the movements needed risks, at the cellular level, the survival of humans for any long-term consideration. Mars has equal concerns as its barycenter force is significantly less than we have on Earth. It has an increased rotational rate which should be viewed as an external spin. This is due to the small core to atmosphere ratio. There are new sciences that need to be presented to serve each astronaut for their short-term and long-term survival. The presentation of rotational ratios within each planet needs to be reviewed for each person with the same diligence.

# Chapter Eight
## Reaching for the Apple

### *Turner's 5th theory of biological gravity*

**The definition of opposition to gravity is not lack of gravity. It is the ability to use opposing movements within the bind of gravity that creates a counter force.**

> *"Gravity. It's not just a good idea; it's the law."*
>
> – Adam Savage

In beginning or immature movements, it is the oppositional interaction between gravity and opposing movements within its bind that initiates the ability to counterbalance. It is different to oppose the force of gravity at that moment. Turning a page of this book is functional movement in opposition to gravity. Bringing your fork to your mouth is functional movement in opposition to gravity. Lifting your arm out to the side is not functional movement in opposition to gravity. It might look like it's opposing gravity, because it is. However, it is not a functional movement. No life-based task can be achieved while performing that movement. You will not see a baby do this movement. If you do, the child is organizing to a risk of or similar to cerebral palsy. Doing a deadlift from a squat, is a load/lift muscle-based movement but it is not a functional movement. Both of these non-functional movements have a muscle dominance of lift, which is not the same as rotational movement towards function. Yes, non-functional movements can increase muscle response, size and range of motion, but you will never be able to increase function based on those movements. Here's one of the key things I recently discovered. Science believes that your mass is the same no matter where you are in the universe. However, there's a difference between the mass of a piano and the mass of a human being. The inter-relationship of a being's buoyancy changes all functions based on its ability to respond to this force in various positions, neurology, and health. You can have complete mind-over-matter and these forces will supersede if you do not know how to work with them. Depending where I am in space and what my neurological adaptations are to counter or use rotational movements, then buoyancy varies. Buoyancy in living beings changes how a body's mass responds to movement and organization. Therefore, gravity is not a constant because of the differences within my system and your system.

It has been thought that gravity has to do largely with density, which is also related to volume. Mass does stay constant, but the volume and its relationship to buoyancy within a specific gravitational pull may or may not change. This is true for a brick of clay or one of gold. But because I can organize or move with my body's field of buoyancy, my mass responds differently to that of a person with cerebral palsy. This is why they organize succumbing to gravity whereas I organize opposing gravity. However, this is also why human life is rapidly changing. So, if we think that we'd better be jumping off of this rock to Mars, let's not bring all of our outdated Earthly information.

When I stand up, the effort I need to apply is different for me than you due to our individual relationship with gravity, from our organization within. The application of a visual copying or manipulation of movement changes to a muscles-based manipulation rather than natural gravitational response that includes the use of muscles. New cellular metrics also need to be included for the calculations of interior momentum.

Going back to cellular movement dynamics. Let's look at the way blood moves. Does blood move? Yes. Can it be measured? Yes. The blood of a baby, with no muscular, skeletal or emotional friction, has not had any exposure to a food source prior to birth. The mother's blood movement dynamics and viscosity rate are the only aspect a fetus has to interpret in amniotic gravity. Therefore, blood-based responses of an infant have to move more efficiently than the way my body processes the entire circulatory system.

One of the first breakdowns of interior momentum abilities can depend on the water weight during the fetal/neonatal period. The introduction of gravitational pressure to blood movement of a premature one KG baby to a full-term three and a half KG baby would need more pressure for the rate. Now we can increase the ratio of pressure, rotational response and buoyancy presented in gestational diabetes where, not only is the amniotic fluid heavier, changing the expansion rate or pressure to the fetus but the actual weight and internal pressure of the baby has increased. The subtle viscosity or fluid to weight organization to a compromised system can change the way the newborn processes movement. Add a little jaundice and a few days in the Neonatal Intensive Care Unit to the first few days of life and you will alter the organization of movement dynamics in the body.

Using the same analogies within the human body, the same system processes can be experienced in astronauts in outer space. They are exposed to the same biomechanics as a child with special needs. Contained in their experience is lack of rotational movements in opposition to gravity unable to perform any functional movement, as defined on Earth. Science has not taken into account these movement metrics in astronauts, prior to space travel, and then instantly noted changes in their lives/bodies when they leave Earth. The theories presented in this book are based within the structures of movement within and without the abilities to oppose gravity. You might be thinking that this is a muscle based force, but it's actually a system based force. Blood dynamics alone can destroy the body in long term space based living. Changing the exterior movement ratios in the use of exercise based on functional movement is the first shift needed in this equation. A century ago, man shifted to modern living scenarios. If Einstein were born a half a century, pre or post his observations, he might not have been on a train for his inspiration. Nor would I have the visual reference of the US Space Shuttle for mine. We cannot continue with the immature functions of biomechanics for humanity's survival in multi-planetary living conditions. Equally so, the best person to first represent those conditions is not necessarily the fittest.

Premodern age, almost all movement that an adult produced was functional. Removing those with affluence, directing our attention to those creating and satisfying needs for our survival, they needed functional movements to bring their produce to the community. During activities like bailing hay, farming, herding livestock, sewing, washing and cooking, rotational movements were above the shoulder, producing constant motions in opposition to gravity with rotation. Since more of the population is now dominantly affluent, the number of people who still move in this fashion is almost down to twelve percent. This doesn't mean money-based affluence but societal-based. Most of us have not raised our hands above our shoulders in years. Equally alarming to the loss of functional movement is the increase of weight, disease, boredom, lack of communication and problem solving. We are now passing the momentum loss to our babies through product use.

Your blood with a sugar of 500 is heavier than a sugar of 92. However, your movement vocabulary is also substantially reduced. For you, too, this isn't about exercise, this is about functional movement. This isn't to say that if you increase your movements to include constant rotational movements in opposition to gravity, you will automatically be disease free. Rather you will be able to stabilize and organize your system through natural physics within those of biological gravity. The current NASA movement program is designed around load/lift containment equipment securing astronauts so their bodies may stimulate cardiovascular changes. However, it doesn't relate to the system neurologically, so it doesn't take. Therefore, the rotational dynamics changes in the blood's ability to use and process, move and place nutrition throughout the body. These complications continue, causing sugars and enzymes to increase cellular stress. Sugars compress on the nerves because of the increased weight but change the rotation in the fluid and/or cells within the body. Protein also has a unique rotational rate. Cancer, as a mass response, would not have a rotational rate that could be functional. Also, it would need to aggravate the natural rotational rate of necessary cells, red and white blood cells, changing their ability to function due solely on the inability to rotate in opposition to gravity therefore killing the system.

Depending on the amount of movement needed for me to walk to my car can instantly be changed within this ratio. Remember, my definition of functional movement is movement that goes through the large and small organs. This is why you are supposed to walk if you are a diabetic; to change the cellular dynamics the sugar is affecting. This is why the movement needed is functional with rotation in opposition. But what if you can't walk because you are too 'heavy' or your viscosity rate has changed so that you can no longer organize functional movements?!

BINGO!! This is what happens to astronauts. They are technically not heavy; in space, I can lift anything. Yet in the involvement of the lift, my body will not respond with functional, rotational movements! To continue with these immature and exterior, repetitive movements thinking that man would or could survive is why all of mankind is finding frustration for degenerative disorders. This is most evident in the twin study and offers an explanation for DNA restructuring between the Kelly Astronauts. In a helical presentation, they are no longer the same. The cellular rotation needs opposing force found in its interplay with gravity. I can't stress enough that we also need to change our gravitational interaction of just falling. All the apples are not falling off the tree. Just the ones that have changed, therefore lost, the ability they need to offer buoyancy and rotation.

What if instead of a reading of 226 sugar, I got a message on my phone that said, my blood weight just increased by 58%. Based on my current BMI - I need to walk and work the room for 22 minutes or the equivalent of 3/4 mile. Yes - this is where we could have a diet book - not eat for your blood type but eat for your rotation. Protein, sugar, and other biological circulatory cells have different rotational weights. One of the biggest issues that we have with 'junk' food is that it not only never lived, it never rotated. This is a crucial point for Mars colonization, even to grow a plant-based diet on the planet, we would also need to study the internal rotational properties that are offered as part of a food source. Man is very interesting in that we need a variety of food to sustain us. We can't live off of one food source. The structures of these molecules should be in sync within the same matrixes of the human being or organism we are trying to sustain. Interrupting these simple biodynamics will typically produce neurological reasoning disorders, as found with autism and Alzheimer's, as an example. Similar behavior presentations have been found in those who space travel. They don't play well with others.

Absorption can be found in all functional movements. For every action there is an equal and opposite reaction. If I throw the ball at you, you can't ever catch the ball with a flat surface. You need to bend your hand, or actually match the rotation within your field of buoyancy in order to catch it. Einstein noted that space bent, but space has to offer the same inner dynamics. As the Earth orbits, space needs to bend or counterrotate to allow the earth's momentum to maintain this consistent orbit. All orbits organize with the same inner and outer movements. Just as I throw the ball, the movement moves from my body into space.

At the same moment, what if space wasn't bending but scooping or propelling? As the atmosphere bends wind, space needs to offer a binding force with frictionless movements. As the heart and muscles are helical in structure to interact with the movements necessary for life as we know it. As the solar system is helical. The birth of the solar system itself must represent opposition in matter for gravity's binding force to exist.

The object is still bound by my movement, as you see in visual acuity, for the movement to be created more precisely. It's not eye/hand coordination but eye/hand interactions through core movements in oppositional rotations. This is also why vision loss is substantial in outer space.

Imagine moving an object no longer needing inner movements. There is no longer the necessity of eye/hand coordination. More important to note is that there is no longer the need or creation of movement through the core.

## *SPACE-BASED COMPLICATIONS*

Although it is easy to perceive outer space as micro gravity, it is also easy to view an astronaut in a perpetual fall. Equally misleading is the thought that opposition to gravity is the lack of gravity. When we stand up from a chair, we are not only opposing the binding force of gravity, we are also neuro-mapping all calculations based on the force, rotation, and buoyancy needed to do this task and any other functional movements. This is the key criteria about why space depletes our systems from the moment we leave the earth's atmosphere. Within all these functional movements is the creation of a force necessary for our biological functions. Changing our location, i.e. living or traveling in space, does not eliminate or alter our body's need for these same functional movements. Therefore, in space, we need to replicate a functional force that will replicate this cycle rather than create a situation which we refer to as exercise. Replicating gravity is not the answer for our survival, it is maintaining our force generated for opposing gravity. Not only do humans regulate this interaction but it maintains our systems for developmental movements.

New exercises need to be implemented and studied, and so does our ability for spatial interaction; pre, during and post Earth's return. On the International Space Station, social distancing is a constant as astronauts are not going home each day to friends and family. The constant withdrawal in such close quarters is an issue. From simple routines of stretching and lounging to just taking a walk, a run or hitting the punching bag, all of these activities are impossible during the duration of space travel. Not neglecting the push/pull milestones is important to maintain a skeletal constant. They are a significant and often neglected part of our health and global wellbeing. However, in outer space, skeletal movements need to be maintained in conjunction with exercising. Muscles respond to all movements through the binding force that is structured through the skeletal system. Arranging an astronaut's mass variables to their range of oppositional rotational movements prior to flight and post-recovery is needed for their health and expedited recovery.

# SPACE-BASED ADAPTATIONS

Movement applications need to be efficiently organized prior to space travel in order to position our astronauts and space travelers to be able to move in new ways, preparing them to work with the functional force. We can help them by making their bodies more aware of the structural changes they will encounter in space in order to neutralize or redirect the current responsive movements created for task skills to force-based interactions on a daily basis. We can't change our brain and expect our bodies to continue with the same trajectory or improve without the integration. The same concepts can be applied when we are presented with neurological damage.

Our inner movements are based on the foundational movements of living biology. We have fluid and cellular dynamics interacting as one. The introduction of mass differentials to rotational ratios affect all movements from eating to organizing a screwdriver. Mass is not the same from human to human and is rightly so in space-based movements. Understanding the process of movements within the body and throughout is as important in space as it is in life. Calculations need to be devised for each person prior to space travel so that comparisons can be done during each mission. It is within these comparisons of space travel related changes that significant new findings will arise.

# Chapter Nine
## Moving In and Out of Movement

### *Turner's 6th theory of biological gravity*

**It is the inner rotational movement, momentum, and buoyancy that binds one force to another force.**

> *"Here comes the sun, and I say, it's alright."*
>
> – The Beatles

All movements needed for living beings, from humans to planets, have a foundation that includes specific inner rotational movements, movement and buoyancy that creates a binding force, the structure needed to attract all living bodies to each other, from one force to another. This is the creation of gravity but not as a pull or pin, which are linear and static. The most obvious reference is the Earth's inner core. The movement equation, in reference to which, we create or organize our life force. Science has presented that the inner core is a solid ball of iron. This may be true; however, our focus is the movement dynamics. The rotational movement of the inner core can be confused as the acceleration of gravity, which also creates a momentum of a bind where the opposing outer core, a molten fluid, binds to the movement mass of the inner core rotation. However, it is the oppositional rotational movement of these two components of our planet that forms our physical gravity. Fluid dynamics with rotational movement are simple yet significant origins of physical momentum and buoyancy. They are contained by the Mesosphere, regulated by the mantle's inner rotational movement and are now seen as the mantle convection cells. Dynamic core organization containing large pockets of downward and upward force rotational movements are needed to transfer gravity from a two-dimensional rotation. Counter momentum and buoyancy dynamics are needed to create living and moving layers of the crust. From within this rotation water is forced into the mantle, through these currents, forming the thrust and force needed for our life's existence.

For humans and other beings that oppose gravity with functional movement, the spatial relationship comes from their body's ability to create, respond to and interact with buoyancy. When a baby is born, the first dimensional movement to gravity is within its first breath. In natural delivery, there is a simultaneous production that initiates breathing and sucking at the moment of the baby's birth. The unfused skull bones begin to morph and elongate as the baby moves through the birth canal. During this phase, the head begins the body's rotation out of the mother's vaginal canal. This simple act creates a vacuum between the mouth and the palate of the infant like that of a cork coming out of a bottle. When the head has gone beyond the cervix, the tongue strikes the palate to start the sucking mechanics of the newborn. Within this mechanism of cavitation is the production of gases, such as oxygen, nitrogen and carbon dioxide, to aid in swallow mechanics and soft tissue stimulation in the nasal cavities.

The head shape will return to normal in a few days. Breathing initiates muscle glide and buoyancy between the complex levels of structure within the lungs/diaphragm, intestinal/organ cavity and pelvic symphysis. These movement patterns need to be initiated and stimulated from the inside of the body through breath. The body's initial breath goes throughout the chest cavity to the pelvic region. Optimal tongue/palate stimulation should be continued with the act of nursing immediately after birth.

The force or execution of the breath is the neurological stimulation for muscle tonus. There are two reasons for this thought. First, breath is one of the body's first organizations to gravitational force. Anybody that cannot regulate the opposition of gravity in breath cannot regulate gravity in vertical actions. Therefore, a child who has respiratory distress and doesn't receive rotation based therapy immediately after birth will also be challenged in vertical-based gravity milestones. The second reason for this thought has to do with rib expansion and the intercostal muscles.

During a natural delivery, a process called cavitation happens. The head goes into subluxation and creates a vacuum in the mouth palate. That draws the tongue to a snap or pop. The pop stimulates the lung foam to engage to open the lungs from the inside-out. This first breath creates an inner force as gravity is the outer force against the intercostal muscles. Failure in this process means that all the body's muscles do not set up a proper relation to oppose gravity. This lack of stimuli means a low or high tone muscle-based system. Most people believe muscles tonus is only a neurological signal, but all of my clinical experience has shown me that it is not.

Why do I keep talking about the babies? Well, similarly, if you drop an astronaut back to earth, they've lost all vertical milestone accomplishments. It's the same developmental movement patterns as a child. This is due to the fact that they can never create these milestones due to the lack of or inability to exhibit or organize rotational movements in opposition to gravity.

Breathing creates a living buoyancy with cellular responses to these phenomenons. We look at atomic density, but what if we actually looked at atomic buoyancy? The theories of living buoyancy differ greatly to that of an inanimate mass. We'll get into that a little bit later.

We commonly think of gold weighing less than lead. We think of the nucleus and electrons when considering the density of the metal or gas. Those objects have mass. Neither will ever change on their own accord. Unless I add the possibility of heat to excite or melt the atoms so that they can change into another visual form, they will remain as they are. If I lay my gold ring on the table, it will never change shape and become another size or shape of ring, nor will it decide to leave the table and go into another room.

When you have a multitude of circles within circles, we know that we can mimic almost any movement. Yet science tries to say that we are the same mass no matter the place in space because my mass is in relation to that planet's gravitational force. It might be true for a weight differential, but not for movement. If you and I were to both throw a ball, we would throw the ball differently. Why? Because you and I have a different organization, not only to rotation, but to cellular buoyancy as well.

How far can you throw a ball if you don't use rotation? Not at all, because you won't even be able to pick it up without using rotation. When learning a movement, and you are trying to imitate, which is an approach used by most therapies and professionals, you attempt to assimilate what you imitate through muscle-based movements. This is not how we learn a new movement. We do so through rotational movements as an interior response.

Remember, there are no linear points on the human body. Development of complex movement patterns (e.g. walking) requires the coordination of momentum and acceleration within our environment with no fixed points of reference. Functional movement builds upon experiences of moving within our environment from the neonatal period forward. An infant, having no experience with movement in a gravitational field, creates unique system mechanics in relation to gravity while lacking the cognitive ability to willfully transfer might against mass. Constraints during this developmental period, either internal or external, can lead to system shutdown or long-term restrictions. The work described here addresses a method of introducing those experiences in order to change the brain and develop these functional system mechanics. Application of gentle external touch is used to guide a client through a rotational movement. Subtle variation is added to increase the complexity of any and all movement. In this method, learning is not accomplished by finding the point of failure or rote repetition. Rather, basic rotational movements are built upon to create the foundations to initiate and enhance interactive transitional and functional movements.

At its peak, the human body moves fluidly in three-dimensional space while maintaining balance and opposing gravity. A healthy system utilizes a vocabulary of complex movements to engage with the environment and move (walking, sitting, standing, etc). We, at Movement Lesson™, define system mechanics as the integration of movements, external stimuli and neurological organization to result into a holistic movement. Movement vocabulary is built from experiences which begin in infancy. Neurologically impaired systems are either unable to initiate exploration or exhibit an improper relationship to gravity. The relationship to gravity is the fundamental underpinning of volitional movement.

Every cell in the human body has a property of living buoyancy. Like a balloon that can go on in any direction, a 360-degree responsive action. The body doesn't use definitive movements like up and down or side-to-side. The worst misconceptions of nonfunctional movement appear in flection and inflection. Those are static visual definitions. At any time, a body can go in and out of transitional movements from any position and/or interaction as an internal action from an external stimulus. Some cellular functions are fixed. The human skeletal system is a structural interactive system, not only in relationship to a constant and, for the most part, a sound structure. To look at the skeletal structure as a solid does the body a serious injustice, for no two bones are the same and no bone is a solid. The skeleton is an intricate, webbed internal structure. The body produces all movements through the skeletal structure and buoyancy to create momentum. Some cells are moving - blood cells for example. Is what you refer to as blood pressure really an aspect of buoyancy and momentum? Some cells are active and passive - muscles.

Are you able to produce power from nowhere due to buoyancy and momentum? Or are your muscles stiff? Tight? or Floppy? It needs to be noted that some cells are mass. A mass, like a brick of gold, will respond to the non-biological responses to gravity. These cells are benign, cancerous, cellular abnormalities. They do not respond with rotation and they don't play well with others. They succumb to gravity. This is one of the key reasons why some people with very little evidence of cancer pass quickly. The living body does not respond to inner counter-oppositional movements. Some are reversed processors or send back a movement. Fatty tissues and fat cells are not inherently dangerous in proportion to the body as a whole. However, like Jello, a movement can hit fatty tissues and rebound, causing the body to have to counter movement versus utilizing core movement. This is not what is commonly referred to as core strength. Just because a person has a form of strength, it doesn't mean that they have or can create functional movements. It is within this interior network of movement gauges that they can create a unique pattern and/or response of movement for that person. The body, through gravity and exterior stimulation, acknowledges where it is spatially for unconscious and cognitive actions. It interacts with all of these cellular principles within the natural theories of biological gravity and buoyancy that creates movements through cognitive interactions.

## POP QUIZ:

**Question #4: What does it take for an inner movement to redirect an outer movement? How many inner movements does it take to stabilize an outer movement?**

## POP QUIZ:

**Question #5: How far can you throw a ball? How far can you throw a ball without rotation?**

## *SPACE-BASED COMPLICATIONS*

The dynamic changes experienced in the interaction and ratios of buoyancy, rotation, and gravity without any form of integration immediately and continually stresses the system. Internal viscosity rates change due to the lack of interaction as the body is now in expansion mode. Suctioning forces now decrease because it would cause friction on the body. In the womb, living beings are not organized for friction. The growing fetus will avoid it at all costs. This is one of the key reasons sleeping is so difficult in a space station. The body is actually avoiding compression, which is necessary for a resting state in order to bring the body back to its absolute horizon.

Lying is an active posture, even in the first few days of life. This crucial milestone is key to arranging short-term and long-term movement and stimuli responses that includes cognitive neuro-mapping.[2] The body's relationship to an absolute horizon, within the first weeks of life, allows the system to develop and mature.

It is commonly assumed that the human body has the ability to move and organize around its environment. However, the human body needs to have a relationship to an absolute horizon in order to initiate, stimulate, and enhance the organization of movement. Organized movement also results in cognitive development by allowing a newborn to manipulate their reaction to stimulation. At the same time, the human body cannot have an artificial horizon before the system has organized around its absolute horizon. Doctors believe that these planes originate from optical function in relation to the inner ear.[3] Visual and auditory spatial cues bear no fixed relationship to one another, but change dramatically and frequently as the eyes move, about three times per second over an 80° range of space.[4] However, as with a navigational gyroscope, the human body responds to external torque forces through our exterior gravitational force (14.7 psi), creating interior skeletal movements of rotation within the body. These complex actions can only be accomplished when the body has reference to an absolute horizon.

When a newborn baby is in the process of a typical natural delivery and starts to crown, the baby has rotated in position for the head to mold and elongate out of the vaginal canal. After the presentation of the head, the rotation will continue to allow soft tissue to initiate functions as each shoulder exits the womb separately. This continuous action allows lung expansion through cavitation to introduce oxygenation function as the body continues to leave the mother's system. Approximately one-third of fetal lung fluid is removed during vaginal delivery as the chest is squeezed and lung fluid exits through the nose and mouth. This rotation initiates the newborn's system mechanics to have a complete orga-

2 Movement analysis in infancy may be useful for early diagnosis of autism: Teitelbaum, Teitelbaum, Nye, Fryman, Maurer, PNAS November 10, 1998

3 Movement analysis in infancy may be useful for early diagnosis of autism: Teitelbaum, Teitelbaum, Nye, Fryman, Maurer, PNAS November 10, 1998

4 Movement analysis in infancy may be useful for early diagnosis of autism: Teitelbaum, Teitelbaum, Nye, Fryman, Maurer, PNAS November 10, 1998

nization of its horizon.[5] A surgical or preterm birth where the newborn is lacking external and internal experiences of these and many other functions to organize around an absolute horizon in opposition to gravity results in a 'false' or 'non' horizon. This false horizon is introduced to the newborn's system, initiating problematic variations to functional developmental movement patterns.

Within the systematic setup of an absolute horizon, the human subsenses can start their primitive or immature relationship within a natural horizon. During this crucial period, lack of restriction around the body is necessary for optimal short-term and long-term development, as it is during this period that the body is learning to manipulate around the horizon. A typical newborn baby exhibiting the ability to counterbalance with rotation is demonstrating cognitive responses to an absolute horizon in relationship to gravity as they internally respond to these external torque forces. The axis of symmetry is the axis around which the body preserves its shape when rotated.[6] The human body cannot be viewed in this manner; however, the body does offer momentum complexities in relation to angular velocity within these simple yet complex infant neuro-responses. While no two systems are identical, initial responses should be similar within these milestones. An infant's relationship of size and matter to a natural horizon is simple, yet complex, to their unique system.

Cognitive integration of these initial responses continues as a newborn travels through space. The simple act of putting a baby into a prone position is a critical demonstration of the system's cognitive and movement organization. By allowing an unrestricted baby to lie on a flat surface, it is able to create its first neuro-mapping to a primitive spatial awareness for organ integration in a gravitational response. A baby that is in the arms of another human being is responding to or has bonded with that person's gyroscopic functions. Most first-time parents quickly learn that they must walk around the room, not sit, in order to calm their baby's central nervous system. At the same time, a baby that needs or has grown to rely on inanimate gyroscopic functions found in cars, mechanical swings and cribs has their ability to self-regulate and develop natural responses interrupted.

Removing the baby from an adult's gravitational bond and beginning the descent of lowering the baby into a crib initiates a developmen-

5 Developmental trajectories of hand movements in typical infants and those at risk of developmental disorders: an observational study of kinematics during the first year of life. Ouss, L. et al., Front Psychol. 9, 83 (2018).

6 A new paradigm for animal symmetry: Holló 2015

tal milestone. The human body's ability to move up, down, and around its absolute horizon will emerge as a vertical horizon to spatial orientation. A baby that startles, or demonstrates a constant primitive reflex of neuro-response to a degree of waking a sleeping child, or creating the inability to self-soothe has not established or initiated a relationship to its absolute horizon. Therefore, a human's absolute horizon is a boundary in spacetime, as defined in general relativity. This is in respect to the external universe (environment) as it moves within these forces as internal events which include momentum and force.

## *SPACE-BASED ADAPTATIONS*

As we view the constitution of original functional movement patterns within biological systems, we can see that the movement of the human body is based on universally understood scientific principles. Development of the human body relies on the ability to organize automatic interactions within the natural laws while in opposition to gravity. Our environment does not cause movement in our bodies, rather only a stimulus that includes the option of reactive movement. From birth, a baby responding to environmental stimuli is also attempting to balance, counterbalance and stabilize throughout their body. It is during this period that the topical senses (touch, sound, smell, taste and sight) are significant for global development as are the interactions of the sub-senses (balance, counterbalance, succumbing and opposition to gravity, rotation, temperature, acceleration, pain, proprioception and spatial orientation). During the first hours to days of birth, sub-senses like counterbalance allow the topical senses like touch to stimulate and interact with the newborn's cognitive functional development.

It is these same principles we need to establish in outer space. Simple space-based integrations need to be incorporated for astronauts to establish their neutral, absolute horizon in referencing all movements, not tasks, that they need to accomplish in this new environment.

# Chapter Ten

# Move A Little Closer

## *Turner's 7th theory of biological gravity*

**It is thought that mass, not location, is the key to the interaction of gravitational force; however, mass and buoyancy give the gravitational fields the interaction to organize within the opposing force. In living beings, the interaction with gravity as a whole, organizes functional movement and neurological synapses through the equal combination of buoyancy, fluid, and essential rotational movements.**

*"I'm not quite as buoyant as I was in my youth."*

– Malcolm McDowell

As we look into space, mass represents many things. The mass of Jupiter is much more than Earth's, yet Mars is just the size of our core. Currently science uses no representation of rotational mass, just the size of mass to calculate the response of gravity. The statement that all mass is the same, no matter where it is in space, is not true. We can clearly make that statement with an intimate object. I have a cup and it's a cup. It will fall like a cup and stay on the table like a cup. It will respond to gravity and buoyancy within the same characteristics. The increased size of Jupiter should be associated with the same increase in surface gravity for an equal representation of mass distribution. Jupiter is 318 times larger than Earth, yet its surface gravity is just 2.4 times greater than Earth's. Although Jupiter is mostly made up of gases, it's the lack in its core that creates a weak gravitational binding force.

Now let's look at the dark side of the Moon for missing gravity. You can find all sorts of radial gravity anomalies on the surface which impact landing calculations. Here you can see variations of binding pockets that affect our need for constant relationships to our movements in coordination to the Moon's. There needs to be an addendum to the definition of mass. The current teaching is that all mass is the same throughout the universe. This is a guise of gravity and mass, for our bodies are not the same on a minute to minute basis on Earth nor are they in outer space. As you throw a rock into a pond, the impact of surface tension and mass creates a new border in relationship to the shoreline. If you eat a piece of lettuce today, based on your movements of activities and inner body activity, you will never digest, absorb, or eliminate the lettuce in the same manner again. Now if I take a mug to outer space, this will always have the same mass because it is an object. Cancer acts as a mass, due to its lack of rotational movements in opposition to gravity. My inner and outer rotational responses in respect to the Earth will differ on the ISS, Moon, Mars, and anywhere else we care to travel. Just ascending to Mt. Everest, all calculations of mass change just due to viscosity and elimination patterns to air and water. On average, a climber summiting Everest burns 20,000 calories. This is a burn calculation, not a consumption. Concept of mass differential to counter gravity responses need to be examined to benefit the person traveling and interacting with all spatial experiences from Earth to Mars and back once again for them to be able to maintain a responsive binding force needed for functional movements.

Living organisms, which are simple in nature, need different introductions to care. Consider that you have four pea seeds, with the same light, water and properties within the soil, you will have four different plants. The initial response of opposing force as the root shoots into the ground in combination with its rotational movements are key to the seed's ability to oppose gravity and begin to create a plant. As it rises towards, what we've determined, is the light.

Let's look at these movements a little closer. The moment the plant leaves the seed, the momentum of opposing forces and core movements happens at the seed level. The root quickly shoots downward with rotational movements that regulate the strength of the plant. The seedling pushes through the earth with rotational force and is suddenly exposed to the exterior force of gravity. For the plant to continue to grow, it needs rotational movements in opposition to gravity. During its first day, the stem will continue to rise in vertical dynamics. As it continues, the leaves start to shoot out in a horizontal reach to create an additional rotational force, needed to increase fluid and cellular consumption necessary to produce a plant. These two main actions need to happen for the plant to create exterior, not core based, rotation as the tendrils expand out looking for the support needed to produce product and eventually seed.

Keep in mind those movement dynamics and we'll add solar interaction. Our earth is in constant rotational movements. We are taught that it's an elliptical orbit around the sun. It's a bit more complex than that as the earth tries to unravel a small circular loop as it orbits. The inner core rotates in opposing circular movements creating the gravitation bind. At the same time the sun, also rotating, rises in the east and sets in the west. The plant organizes around this exterior rotation. It sleeps at night and will start to reach up to greet the sun. As the sun transfers across the sky, the plant will follow the sun, aiding in the core rotation and will watch the sun set. Not much different than you turning to the right to pick up the box and twisting to put the box up onto the shelf.

Any flower will add to a more complex rotation as it opens in its helical structure and rotates into position of the sun, following with a small yet complex bend to follow the sun's movements across the sky. Until the sun sets and the flower closes with a rotation and bend, to do it the next day.

Let's take these two dynamics needed for life and add atmospheric influence. A water molecule is so sensitive to these complex solar movements that it doesn't fall but rotates as it runs down a drain, depending on the hemisphere, rotates into a level position. All atmospheric motions have properties of rotation, from simple water flow, jet stream, to hurricanes and tornadoes. If you grow a tree in a greenhouse, the tree will die if you do not include a fan in the green house. It's thought that the plants need wind to grow. In actuality, they need the complexities of rotation.

This is no different than the movements needed in a baby's birth and a newborn's movements. It is within these complex rotational interactions that we find the foundations for all developmental movement patterns and gravitational interaction.

When a baby has established its absolute horizon, as a plant shoots out tendrils in opposing rotational movements, so does a baby start to interact with their arms. What is thought to be reflexes, in actuality, are gravitational-based movements needed for more complex interaction. Another aspect of space travel is the loss of or diminished reflexes, which is a key contributor to sleeping difficulties in space. Sleeping medication is the top prescribed medication on the space station. However, the side effect of the drug/body interaction is an additional complication to the loss of movement and will hinder additional biological principles. Horizontal movements needed in sleep, as seen in plants, reset the movements needed for synchronized movements and spatial orientation. We are not pinned to the ground, but we are in constant interaction and organization.

The interaction of sleep or the reset of helical movements also establishes the body's ability for buoyancy and or the rise and setting of inner living dynamics.

We can perceive the strength of a muscle or bone. As an example, we can look at the lack of movements that are unable to be perceived in space. These seemingly minor movements are the apex of humanity's venture into multi planetary exploration. These are some of the fascinating movements needed for cellular and movement interaction that create something as simple as circulatory and respiratory functions to complex movements needed to drive a car, to get out of bed or get a cup off the shelf.

The continual interaction of rising and setting, not up and down, is the key to the biological gravitational theories needed for the creation of buoyancy interaction in all cellular systems and organ function. For all functional movement is an action that includes movement through all these bodily functions.

## *SPACE-BASED COMPLICATIONS*

One of the more noticeable space-based complications in mass and buoyancy ratios in outer space is the response of surface waves. On Earth, surface waves are created at the horizon references, as you would see only on the top of the water or our hair blowing in the wind. In space, water has no horizon reference or a surface point so water or the body experiences surface waves. Human hair is not blowing in the wind but floats outward in all directions. This is one of the first neuromuscular interruptions, creating a diaphragm response around the top of the head within the hair line. This lift creates the first immediate lack of tonus within the muscles ability to respond with force and release.

The second, seemingly simple dynamic, is the collision ratio found in outer space oxygen responses in air bubbles. A simple space experiment is overlooked with the complexities of oxygen regulation as a cellular response found in skeletal buoyancy. In continued studies of astronauts, researchers saw that spaceflight is linked with nutrient shifts, oxygen deprivation stress and more inflammation. What is thought to be presented with the prevention of falling is actually a key component in rising into standing and air release to sitting. Standing and sitting are the two primary milestones that astronauts are unable to perform in any space-based activities. We witness this breakdown in fun tricks of somersaults in anti-gravity. On Earth, it's not that the task can't be performed; the air-bubbles and cellular buoyancy will rise for our natural neurological make-up. In outer space, this feat will be done around a centered bubble, placing crucial stresses and redirection to the brain's ability to produce standard body functions.

"Chronic situations of infection, cancer, and DNA changes were reported in the Twins Study." Christopher Mason, a geneticist at Weill Cornell Medical Center in New York and co-author on the study, said during a teleconference. "As soon as [Scott] got into space, there was a large-scale shift in over 1,000 genes that are actually dynamically changing...so, clearly the body and cells were adapting,"[7]

## *SPACE-BASED ADAPTATIONS*

Preflight organization of oxygen and fluid dynamic responses needs to be introduced to astronauts on an individual basis. One's skin to skeletal ratio needs to be measured then calculated into one's depth muscle to fat mass. Just because someone has a low BMI doesn't mean they have better or more complex movements available to or from their nervous system. An astronaut needs to produce pre-flight introduction of interior movement functions that will be needed to be produced and reproduced in short- and long-term space travel. These new skills must be individually calculated for one's cellular, organ and skeletal maintenance and for sound structure.

The continued understanding of the structure of our bodies is needed from movement. The organization is found within opposing gravity with rotational responses, needed with an equal equation to the natural laws of buoyancy. Space-based adaptations need to be immediately configured to enhance travel and the body's ability to experience it.

---

7 Human Exploration Research Opportunities - Differential Effects on Homozygous Twin Astronauts Associated with Differences in Exposure to Spaceflight Factors

# PART IV
# Beings Interact With Gravity

# Chapter Eleven

## The Structure of Being

### *Turner's 8th theory of biological gravity*

**The basis for all movement is a structure, not an action. For all living organisms, it is not about how gravity behaves, but how we act and interplay with the forces of gravity through responsive movements.**

*"When it is obvious that the goals cannot be reached, don't adjust the goals, adjust the action steps."*

– Confucius

The intertwining forces in opposition to gravity yields what is needed to produce a functional movement which then creates cognitive neuro-mapping. All functional movements are core movements that process at a cellular level. In humans, this movement goes through all major and minor organs. Movements are meant to be created from an internal structure that organizes to the natural forces from within our bodies. Movements in the body are not from an external force. A muscle does not create a movement, it responds to movement. Actions are measurable for the range and amount of force, but they are not the source.

In plants, the oppositional force from the seed pod continues into the functional rotational movements in opposition to gravity. The roots shoot into the ground and counterbalance the forces that are above ground. This key principle is why you can plant two seeds, or a thousand seeds and each plant will be different. Of course, a plant species and humans have countless similarities, but they are different.

We can clearly see that in the twin experiment, the closest compliment, what science thought was due to a cellular structure was actually the DNA and genetic sequencing. As you have been learning, two brothers' cellular data and neurological processes to stress, movement, space and gravity will be unique as with their life-force and failure. In other words, it is a high probability they will not die in the same manner. It is true that siblings may die with the same family history of heart disease or cancer, but the process of how they handle these organizations will be different.

Any plant needs the structure of rotation to grow. Similar to experiences noted in previous points, as the plant is organizing these features there is an exterior attachment to this needed structure. Its mass/might ratio is coordinating with all of its being for life sustaining forces to interact. Once the ratio has been initiated, leaves will form to include articulated rotation from all directions, increasing fluid dynamics in a cellular ratio. Articulated movements interacting with key structures are absolute to bearing fruit. A plant that cannot process this foundation cannot move into a production phase later in life. The main reason is the plant is now yielding to succumbing to gravity and will experience death or be in survival mode.

Space takes away this internal processing. This is why we study plant growth in anti-gravity. What is not studied is plant life with anti-rotational abilities or responses. You will have some opposition or similarities to life on earth if there is soil. The mass/might ratio is in play as the roots move through the soil and the plant is growing in opposition.

These are close to what is needed for humans in movement-based activities and exercises in space. Not the pinning of the feet but the creation of interaction of force.

The same similarities to a plant can be found in getting out of bed. The ability to rise out of bed rather than forcing yourself to get out of bed is the key to increased life forces. When mass/might ratios are too high for a human, they struggle to get out of bed and other simple transitioning skills. When a baby's mass/might ratios are too high to experience tummy time, life functions activities complications present. It's no surprise to me when a baby who is unable to interact, and must be placed in tummy time also has swallowing and feeding complications. Solution: a baby, who is unable to roll in and out of tummy time at 2.5 months should be given an evaluation and therapy techniques that will help with feeding. Yet, using the evaluations available in common practice today, a baby first needs to fail their swallow study, fail to move into purees, fail to move in and out of the breast or formula, when the two actions are interrelated. In the same vein, this errant evaluation process related to infants is parallelled in how we approach movement in space. This is why you can't get to Mars without me! The body's complexities of inter-relationship to tasks and milestones are overlooked and observed as a cognitive interaction versus a global or body response.

Just as the interactions of a mass/might ratio being lost in space creates issues with tissue and cellular regeneration on an astronaut's body, changes and increases of oils, dirt, and dead skin cells are enough 'weight' on a body to create sensory issues. Adding the emotional toll that self-care has on the other astronauts equally shuts down natural responses. As noted by Col. Chris Hadfield, just clipping his fingernails and having them get into the air ducts and propel against others and equipment; a simple task now has complexities and repercussions.[8] This issue goes above and beyond needing privacy. Changing the dynamics of responsive movements to dynamic interactions of a colony changes life force structures. How an individual astronaut handles their personal relationships through rank versus friendship completely changes any and all living movements of humans.

---

8 An Astronaut's Guide to Life on Earth: What Going to Space Taught Me About Ingenuity, Determination and Being Prepared for Anything: Hadfield , 2015

## *SPACE-BASED COMPLICATIONS*

The need for constant vigilance in a rank-based environment causes immediate complications on all inner and outer movement responses. Adding to these complications, a rote form of mimic and order, although necessary in this volatile and dangerous situation, does not allow for any spontaneous or individual interactions of self or colony. Changing movement dynamics has an immediate effect on internal structure dynamics. This is where we try to prove that certain types of stress or how we handle or not handle stress can cause cancer and/or heart disease. Not permitting a person to move in and out of a situation is the key for system failure. This is equally a classic example of special needs. I refer to movement or a milestone as a transitional skill. A baby is never on all fours. A baby is or should be moving in and out of all fours from the belly, sitting, and/or crawling. An equally spontaneous interaction of moving in and out of something. A child with special needs does not have this quality of movement. Therefore, most therapies try to adapt static achievements that have nothing to do with spatial interaction or going in and out of movements through interactions or combinations of skills.

It is necessary to have very precise tasks, manipulations, checks and cross checks of procedures that include manuals. All tasks in outer space need to be performed with an exactness or static achievement. A complete opposite of how an astronaut got to their position on the space station.

## *SPACE-BASED ADAPTATIONS*

Although it is extremely important and life-sustaining for all those on the space station to maintain a level of expertise and exactness that is found in very few environments, an astronaut needs physical activity and human interaction that includes movement structure(s). Astro therapy needs to include two person or group exercises that involve push/pull, spontaneous and play activities. Tug of war is an excellent example of going back to passing bales of hay or water in a line. Adapting a space-based interaction found in martial arts or rock climbing can be established with very little space and equipment but is needed for emotions and movements that include aggression management, movement and muscle structure organization, to sleep.

Human beings are in a constant bombardment to be able to change, enhance and limit their own existence by changing their functional muscle mass. Therefore, this perpetual idea that human locomotion is only as efficient as is the muscle or quality of muscle, continues to limit mankind as a whole. In contrast, we need to be thinking that because there are limits within muscle mass and muscle function, human locomotion is not possible from a muscle contraction. Nor is it the quality of man's muscle that limits or stops man's production of a task. It is movement that combines the actions of momentum and mass through the opposition to gravity that will most effectively improve man's locomotion and cognitive function.[9] This erroneous understanding perpetuates the notion that limitation is due to earth's gravitational pull and the percentage of a body's mass which consists of muscles. The study of mass or muscle mass function is also limited to the time in that person's life where mass supersedes the might.

9 Perpetual Motion in Human Beings: The Relationship of Movement and Acceleration in Locomotion; Turner 2016.

# Chapter Twelve
## No Two Humans are the Same

### *Turner's 9th theory of biological gravity*

**Rotational movements are the source of gravitational interaction between living organisms.**

### *Turner's 10th theory of biological gravity*

**Humans organize all cognitive and physical manipulations based on internal and external interactions through the body's ability to respond with and exhibit rotational movements.**

> *"The nitrogen in our DNA, the calcium in our teeth, the iron in our blood, the carbon in our apple pies were made in the interiors of collapsing stars. We are made of starstuff."*
>
> – Carl Sagan, Cosmos

Similar to the Big Bang theory, living organisms need to be birthed in order for their biological gravity to interact with other natural forces creating their optimal strength and structure. The beginning of life might start with the seed; however, the act of birth is needed when the force from within matches the exterior force. It is from within this interaction that a seed starts to produce a plant, as the roots and leaves have an equal and opposite force needed to create core movements. As the root shoots down into the soil, the opposing suckling sprouts need to break through the earth causing the force of rotation. When this opposing force is not introduced, the plant might grow and yield fruit, but in a different manner, similar to a weed that lacks structure.

The architecture of movement is not an action, but a basis of all life force organization. The force of gravity is present around the seed, creating a magnetism of effort in equal response back. For mammals, a baby presents through the contractions of the womb which needs to match the exterior force of gravity for an equal aspect of thrust. This also creates equal rotational movement to stimulate the brain's ability to create cognitive interaction. Removing these movements destroys the body's available interactions for function. It is not possible for living organisms to redirect from this crucial law of interacting in these natural principles.

It is within this inter-development that a plant wicks water and life processes for continued success. A gardener knows that any tree will die in a nursery without wind. In actuality, the wind is causing the plant to rotate. This allows the sucking or opposing force of water to be drawn up, allowing flowers and fruit to be developed. This same principle is found in the human heart, which is actually helical in structure, to draw or suck blood up into circulation with inner rotational movements.

You can see functional rotation in a sunflower: a simple, beautiful plant that produces an edible protein with a wonderful bloom, which originates from a seed planted into the ground. Germinated, it grows a root in opposition to the seed, creating a birthing force similar to that of a child. It then thrusts the plant through the earth's surface as a seedling. The leaves immediately interact with counterbalance and rotation in opposition to gravity and the roots continue to grow in the same principles. Newton was correct: there are opposing forces present that match each other. However, rotation is the movement needed to oppose the force or friction of gravity. That plant continues to grow showing obvious rotational movements, the force needed to wick water through the root system as a lift force. The sunflower quickly organizes to the sun's rotational binding force in order to do this. Some may say that the sun's gravitational force is actually too far away for us to be affected. Or is it? Alone, the light source also initiates a rotational response rising from the East drawing a plant to its gaze until dusk. In sleep, the dormant flower navigates with the Earth core rotation only to, once again, look for the sun.

As the stem or the structure of the plant has established itself, the design of the leaves' thrust is also mathematical architecture that includes counter-rotation. The leaves' structure dynamics are designed to aid the plant's rotational momentum. Whorled leaves offer variations in plants that have a decussate or tricussate or, in the alternate structure of distichous and fibonacci spiral, as the rotational movements oppose gravity in three-dimensional articulated movements through space.[10]

---

10 Decoding the Mathematical Secrets of Plants' Stunning Leaf Patterns, Maddie Burakoff 2019

Many people see a plant reaching for the sun when they should see a unit in opposition to gravity.

Take a moment to imagine a flower opening up to the sun. We all know that the folded blossom has already been created at a rotation. The blossom seeks the bind of the sun's light and as a response, opens, using rotational movements in opposing gravity. The sun is rotating through the sky as the sunflower is following its light source in a synchronized manner. As the sun starts to set, many flowers dip or close to sink into the rotational movements of the night, only to start the process all over again in the morning. When the plant ceases to rotate, it dies.

A few interesting notes: a plant that is being developed through hydroponics may yield a product, but it does not have the same structure noted as above. A plant born from hydroponics has not been 'birthed' into opposition of gravity with rotational movements. It responds more like a vine with less ability for strength, as it needs support from humans. The Earth's rotation continues to create jet stream dynamics as the wind produces atmospheric rotation that our living ecosystems need for all of our vertical sub-senses. These vertical sub-senses are needed for vertical organization or what we refer to as a sense of space.

It doesn't take a rocket scientist to realize that fish and plants can get crowded and start to suffocate. Again, the common denominator in the weakness is the lack of rotational movements. One might say that a simple organism doesn't use functional movements in opposition to gravity. This is true, and therefore, they organize to succumb to gravity.

# POP QUIZ:

**Question #6: Compare the sun's rotational influence on the wind and water. What is more significant to fluid viscosity rate and a plant's survival? Can we rotate a plant in outer space rather than offer it wind and surface tension?**

## *SPACE-BASED COMPLICATIONS*

All circulatory responses need this structure of movement to move fluid dynamics. Outer-planetary challenges can also include viscosity rate changes. Human and plant-based dynamics need to consider changes in fluid dynamics, which are naturally rotational responses but are also weight and quality responses. My blood is going to respond differently to a piece of lettuce, cup of coffee with cream and sugar, pasta, or taco compared to your body fluid interaction. A person's inner rotational abilities need to be studied for informed nutrition intake when in space.

The swirl of the air around a tree creates rotation that is necessary to lift water from the roots into the leaves. Plants and humans need the sensation of opposition to gravity for the organization of life to begin and continue. The simple act of a butterfly squeezing out of a cocoon seems so innocent. However, if that butterfly had human intervention of releasing it from the cocoon, it will never know how to fly.

Changes with inner skeletal rotational movements could be key to bone strength and density issues found with short and long-term space travel. The lack of individual bone skeletal movements needed for human counterbalancing counts for a large part of this conversation. The lack of thrust between circulator and bone structure could reveal the solution to DNA and mitochondrial changes. These are two areas of concentration to address autoimmune failures in the space station.

## *SPACE-BASED ADAPTATIONS*

Current science leads us to believe that changing the direction or the source of the origin of gravity is in the best interest of our current space program. However, our interaction within our ecosystem and interstellar relationships need to be viewed with new mathematical equations, studies and development. One of the most undervalued studies is that of the rotations in the jet streams. Recent studies show that the movement complexities within the jet streams are diminishing and getting longer. Studies need to be introduced to look at the changes, not only in an atmospheric coordination to increased water temperatures, but also with salination and reef changes to living organisms, including mankind. The evolution of man depends on this information for existence on this planet and beyond.

One key study that should be identified is the increase in autism and severe changes in jet stream. Since the late 80's jet stream dynamics have been changing due to increased temperatures and rising water levels. Does the Earth's movement have a complex place in our human biology? Are we as sensitive as a water molecule? Do the changes in the Earth's dynamics affect man's movement, and therefore, cognitive responses cannot initiate as needed for neuro-typical development? One of the keys to this comes from the Kelly twin study showing changes in DNA during the one-year duration of separation during space travel. Lack of gravity is one dimension to cellular changes. The structure of movement is altered in expansion mode with lack of rotational responses.

The current thought that living organisms develop a system of resistance or immunity to gravity or gravitational immunity (GI) is preposterous. The significance of the act of birthing is crucial to survival. From the force of the plant breaking from the seed or a baby breaking from the uterus through the vaginal canal introduces both systems to the force and opposition to gravity for continual growth and learning. In both systems, their first movements that include rotation are similar to escape velocity seen as the shuttle leaves earth's atmosphere. Their ability to oppose gravity must and will include varying degrees of measurable rotation. This increased knowledge of ability to move and increase strength and precision can be done with increased combinations of rotation and mass acceleration. The controlled and spontaneous qualities of speed and rotation can be initiated and enhanced, despite genetics and trauma, with internal and external stimulation. Since the human brain learns by the obvious comparisons of opposite trials, play stimulation is just as, if not more important than, controlled training simulations.

# Chapter Thirteen
## You've Got to Move It

### *Turner's 11th theory of biological gravity*

**The more abilities are increased in both rotational movements and buoyancy, the more a living organism can move in opposition to gravity. The two regulate the response of the internal processes to create locomotion in oppositional space.**

> *"If you move something 10 pounds through space and then stop suddenly, there's a little overshoot. When you transfer weight from one leg to another, there's a certain way that it happens.."*
>
> – Brad Bird

The skeleton system is key for the structure of movement responses in opposition and succumbing to gravity. It's the first scheme to offer a movement stimulus 360 degrees to and away from the floor. Equally important to recognize, the skeletal system is the foundation to respond to movement, not the muscles. We also have many inner rotational functions to counter these movements. An astronaut is one of the most amazing people on Earth. They volunteer for the complete unknown to explore the possibility of life on another planet, interstellar travel and interaction with other solar systems. We need to transfer this information so their bodies can not only adapt, but thrive in new spacial climates. Therefore, we cannot colonize Mars or space without creating oppositional rotational movements in opposition to gravity. Biosciences need to be redirected to require this in organization.

Presenting all of these new universal formulas is a bit of a task. For years, I assumed that math and science knew about movement through gravity. There is a great deal of frustration in having a child 10 weeks premature who spends 37 days in the Neonatal Intensive Care Unit (NICU) only to be told to "wait and see what happens." It is equally frustrating proving aspects of hypotonia to an astronaut.

In the 15th century, the first painting was produced with depth perception. In 1415, Florentine architect Fillipo Brunelleshi painted the Baptistery in Florence. This is the first known artwork depicting linear perspective. Until that time, humanity viewed the world as flat. This is not the same as the Earth being flat, although that conversation was also happening during those times. Just as one of Kepler's laws that an imaginary line sweeps out to equal areas to equal times. In perspective drawing, an imaginary horizontal line is placed within the painting. Then, to a set vanishing point, equal lines are spread out throughout the painting to present an illusion of the depth of field. This brought man's eye from a two-dimensional space into an imaginary three-dimensional representation of space. From there, Galileo helped us to look up and out as we started to look to the skies for new opportunities.

Going back to the earth - they say gravity is a centrifugal force due to earth's rotation around its axis. But there is no axis. Each layer of the core is a rotation against another rotation.

Here's what we don't know about gravity.

1. the origin of gravity.
2. how we organize within gravity.
3. how to interact with it.
4. the immature to mature levels of interaction.

Even though the human body is not organized for exterior movements, most observations of accomplishments are valued by exterior performances. Why is that? Functional movement is movement that goes through all major and minor organs. To have more movement, a person needs more stamina. Most people view stamina as power. For instance, you may often hear people claim that, "I need to work out a lot harder for more endurance." What if I told you that if you reduce friction, you have more stamina? One's ability to move better with rotational movements in opposition to gravity equates to less friction in those movements.

What happens when you shoot a bullet from a gun? The bullet needs rotation to propel it in order not to succumb to what we know as the gravitational force of Earth. We are told that the more friction the bullet endures equates to less distance. If I had an atmosphere of no friction, would I shoot myself in the back as the bullet circled or orbited the Earth? Or do we now see it that, as the bullet maintains rotation and momentum, it circles, or orbits, the Earth. Getting back to the atomic definition of Feynman, do we walk on the Earth, or do we instead orbit it?

I was recently asked by a client of mine, "I put my baby daughter on the physio-ball to play. When did she learn not to fall off, or who taught her?"

First, we are defining that action as a fall. Falling isn't a concept for a healthy human body. It's not to say that we don't fall down, but we also organize or relate to those concepts. We move in opposition to gravity. It's just that simple. Therefore, a baby does not have to be strong in order to move. But they should have stamina. There have been enough studies done matching a baby to a football player. They can't keep up with the baby. One of the reasons is that, when the baby responds to stimulus with rotational movements, there are no bad movements. One of the key failures to mature actions comes from the self-doubt of one's actions and incorrectly achieving movement. Because of that, if you placed a compromised or developmentally delayed baby on the same ball, they will start succumbing to gravity and both the baby and ball will fall. Mankind is doing the same to astronauts in space stations. It's almost like we're putting them on a physio-ball and expecting them to know how to not fall. Yet under normal development or circumstances, you don't have to teach a system not to fall.

I do want to add that in a truly compromised system or human body, entire movement conversations with anything that they do operate under the thought of "do not fall." That person might not understand the word fall, but their body has organized in that manner. It is also worth noting that people do not typically ask how to make a baby stronger. It is only in one's definition of weakness that the force of strength or quality of strength comes into question. The same can be said for reflex integration, as reflexes are also gravitationally based. A parent does not seek to improve gross or fine motor skills. The actions that are required for a baby to develop are answered within the organization of gravity. All of these movements are naturally occurring as a child responds to stimuli through rotational movements. Life is so innocent when you don't have to teach a child how to move. However, if a child's movements are restricted, their deviations and abilities for this interaction to happen changes and result in special needs.

# POP QUIZ:

**Question #7: Can you get up from a lying position without using inner rotational movements?**

# POP QUIZ:

**Question #8: How many hours can you go mimicking a 6-month-old child?**

There is one wonderful exception to this rule, Dr. Stephen Hawking. Diagnosed with ALS in his twenties, he quickly realized that his body would soon lose all function, so he decided to do all that he could to protect his brain. I don't know of any other human being that chose the brain over the body in a similar situation. For most people, the deterioration of simple physical movements, such as holding a cup or a toothbrush, create immediate neurological deviations to the nervous system. Organizing for a different, possibly more efficient way of doing something seems to be out of the picture. The brain becomes obsessed, not necessarily to hold the cup, but of the inability to hold the cup. These are some of the deviations in any and all movements, resulting in changes to cognitive formatting and interactions. You're really not working to develop your child.

Our every movement interacts with the central nervous system cognitively, creating the normal neurological maps that typically can't be taught, as they are based off of the interaction of these natural laws. Human beings just expect things to happen. It's when it doesn't happen and when that failure is present that the world becomes perplexing and we wait for the brain to figure it out. We fail to realize that it's the movement's interaction with the brain that satisfies these points. When we don't understand gravity, there is no way to fully understand movement. If time is relevant, so is movement. This is what was observed in the clocks of Berlin: not that time could not exist in the same manner to each of us, but that movements could not exist in the same manner to each of us.

We need to stop looking at the process of falling. The only way that we can interact, strive, and engage with the natural laws of gravity are with rotational movements and the principles of buoyancy. That's it. A child doesn't learn not to fall, as it isn't even a concept in a baby's brain or body responses.

## *SPACE-BASED COMPLICATIONS*

Losing aspects of the human body is one of the first things to happen in any space agency. The mind is equally fragile. The body cannot organize without these key movement principles. Gravity-based reflexes will either be non-existent or hyper-responsive. It is thought when a reflex is not presented or is overrepresented, they are flight or fight based. However, no baby will know these experiences without a prior experience. Therefore, if they don't present in the reflex, they can't prevent a reflex.

It is within this knowledge that man must rethink the origins of movement within the mass. In contrast, a newborn is not born with a functioning mass of muscle. In neuro-typical development, there are varying degrees of muscles within the system mechanics of the baby. At the same time, the organization of that baby's system is first responding to that of gravity and the effects of gravity to its nervous system. The simple, yet complex act of birth, happens to most living organisms. There is a hatch or release from a contained system as the new organism presents in its own ecosystem. This birth stimulates an immediate response to its own gravity around and through its system. A newborn is forced through the vaginal canal at a varying rate of speed and force. Many factors include the size of the mother and the child, cervical room, contraction rate, genetics (rare disease and disorders), gestational age and education, to name a few. It is this force or birth that exposes that system to that of gravity. The fluid in the brain, in its own enclosed system, creates a similar situation as with a balloon creating a hardened shell being the skull enclosing the force of gravity on the brain. The vacuum that is created from the head first positioning, snaps the tongue from the pallet that initiates the suck reflexes as the lungs are forced from the mother's canal to suddenly expand in life. The epidermis protects general organ and muscle function as it learns to oppose gravity with rotation. It is this opposition to gravity that is most significant for any and all development in a living organism. For when these crucial movements do not initiate within the body's system mechanics failure in the system occurs.

## *SPACE-BASED ADAPTATIONS*

It is believed that the body uses muscles to perform any and all physical tasks, but there has been little discussion regarding invitation of those muscle functions in the human body to form and respond.

Within an action potential of a muscle contraction the size of the muscle will change, a contracted muscle cannot create movement within itself. It is important to note that involuntary muscle functions (ie, cardiac and respiratory) and sub-senses (ie, balance and counterbalance) should remain as a subconscious and automatic response in the nervous system. Skeletal muscles as well as involuntary muscles can be manipulated to become an automatic and deliberate cognitive response depending on the individual's stage of development.

Mature cognitive development varies from increasing new learning practices to enhancing established neuropathways to changing and enhancing muscle strength and movement patterns. The ability to maintain physical mobility increases with various forms of physical exercise. Core strength, abdominal muscles and enlarged bicep muscles are desired outcomes for function and anti-aging. In contrast, understanding the human body's natural ability of perpetual motion will increase system mechanic functions. It is movement that combines the actions of momentum and mass through the opposition to gravity that will most effectively improve man's locomotion and cognitive function.

# Chapter Fourteen

# Binding Gravity Changes with Cellular Interaction

## *Turner's 12th theory of biological gravity*

**For any and all functional actions, using rotational movement can make gravity appear weaker.**

## *Turner's 13th theory of biological gravity*

**Gravity is not felt in outer space because there are no oppositional rotational movements. The binding force of gravity within living beings can only interact through internal rotational movements; otherwise one is more dominant than the other.**

> *"We can't feel the rotation of the planet, but in some ways we can because our bodily systems are reacting to it and have it inherent in them. To me, that's such a powerful thought."*
>
> – Jessa Gamble

The first successful movement in the human body is the expansion of its system in breath. At the same time, the body was meant to rotate out of the vaginal canal, stimulating the act of movement and cognition. The second successful movement in the human body is weight transfer. The third successful movement in the human body is skeletal buoyancy. It is within these key processes that the human body can create a three-dimensional system that interacts within the force of gravity.

The observation of a girl doing a cartwheel is thought to exhibit centrifugal forces as her legs go over her head to the other side. In actuality, each hand reaches or extends to the ground in a coiled rotation from the inner muscles structure reflected into the arm. Her entire system must be able to rotate or twist to initiate all actions. As the spine starts to spring over her body, her legs and feet reach into the opposition of gravity in counteraction to the arms and body. The eyes are equally independent in a rotation that is of the vestibular that includes the inner ear, nasal cavities and uvula. The rotation needs to continue as the feet reach for the floor. This momentum now brings the hands up into the air to mimic the actions of the feet. As long as this equation continues, so will the actions of the cartwheel. All representations of this and other actions can be initiated, enhanced, stimulated for progression or regression with equal momentum.

One of the ultimate workout locations for exceptional athletes is located in Boulder, Colorado. The combination of high altitude and the Continental Divide is thought to contain changes in muscle and lung function to change the levels of endurance of the human body. Typically, lung function is regulated through the air intake going into your nasal cavity and is matched with the soft tissue response in your soft palate. The body then matches this response and draws the lungs into its breath. Infants who have been intubated do not get the neurological experience of breathing or regulating gravity through breath as a missing first life experience. A similar experience can be found on the ISS. Their bodies are unable to feel the new intake due to conditions of the microgravity. The lungs are also not getting a regulated airflow absorption due to the lack of gravitational stimulus on the expansion and retraction. A newborn, unable to regulate the gravitational force of breath, will need therapy or assistance for all vertical milestones. This natural response is true for our astronauts returning to Earth's challenges.

In North America, water will flow towards the Atlantic from the east side and Pacific from the west side. The additional use of fluid counteraction with rotation and counteraction need to be noted in this equation. This section of the earth's core leads to changes of inner direction that cannot be created with human intervention. The surface tension is apparent to the human body through the foot surface. In the example of centrifugal force from a machine it will create an abnormal binding source but from a single direction. Neither the human body nor other organisms are meant for that momentum to its nervous system. The most obvious mathematics in this equation include measurable G-force levels that can be measured by equipment. At this moment, the earth is spinning at a rate of roughly 1,000 miles per hour. If a person were to jump into the air, they would not be hit by a moving wall or tree, nor would the person suffer bodily harm or motion sickness. The nervous system is organized around that movement. Likewise, that person could not stand on an object, such as a car or airplane without suffering injury or even death. Indirectly, humans orbit the earth or interact with the earth's surface.

If you look at conversations to the question, what if the earth stopped spinning? The common answer is we would fly off this rock. Part of the sensation in an astronaut's internal mechanics when they hit space is that lack of rotation equals flight. People who have discovered the thrill of interacting with inanimate objects, rotation and momentum are known to be thrill seekers. The objective of movement becomes their life force. In extreme cases, leaving jobs and families to surf, bike or ski in combination with speed. When a body organizes around a force of movement that comes from the foot surface, changes in the vestibular and cognitive process occurs. The organization around a source of movement is not how man is constructed. Offering objects that change the momentum of man's movements, from phones to surfboards will not propel the evolution of mankind.

The opposite can be found with lack of movement. In nature, the combination of the earth's rotation with that of the directional challenge of the sun creates the thrive of a plant reaching for the sun with movement. Movement is the source of life for all living organisms. A plant that can no longer move, will die. There are some cases of succulents that exhibit life in extreme conditions; however, shown in slow motion, there is movement in the structure of the plant. Little is exhibited in nature that offers a straight line. Thus, allowing the movement of the elements to move around to enhance life.

As we look into the system of the human body, the intricate way that our living mechanisms organize are fascinating. It is thought that man is a load/lift system of levers and pulleys as noted in the study of biomechanics. Many are taught that the contraction of a muscle creates movement through the sliding filament theory. The recent introduction that the collection of myosin/action function based on a synchronized rotation changes the theory of muscle mechanics to two organized and oppositional movements created locomotion. Taking that view to a deeper level, as a person reaches for a cup, the system is countering the action through the body, at the same time that the arm moves forward, an immature system will counteract with the opposing leg. The bones within the arm are moving forward as the muscles are pulling back in an active and passive phase. This same action is performing within the cardiovascular, nervous and respiratory system (to name a few). The movement in a healthy nervous system is bonded throughout the body for optimal performance. To be clear, optimal is equal to easiest or most efficient. By no means is this optimal movement. It is within this equation that some of us are phenomenal at some things and others are with everything. An astronaut needs to be intuitive, educated, humble, a team member, an engineer and a capable individual all at one time.

## *SPACE-BASED COMPLICATIONS*

All living organisms not only lose the sensation of gravity but its interaction that includes rotation and buoyancy. Any ability they have acquired in life, if not recognized and acknowledged, will cease in outer space. Equally, all internal processes fail to create and sustain locomotion and eventually life.

Many people have not participated in genetic testing due to not wanting to know if their bodies have higher risk for a type of cancer or diabetes. Part of the process avoidance is not wanting to suddenly think when and where they will have cancer. That concept of thinking about it brings it closer, from if, to when. The same argument is made for why you wouldn't want to know. So, you may change diet or habits to avoid this predisposition and redirect genetics.

When a person enters space, part of their daily protocols is how to avoid death. Not only dying, but how to handle the process of death. From getting a body home, letting the family know, telling the ground crew. Yet, for most astronauts, due to their training prior to space, they have a much higher ratio of loss of life. Pilots and those in the service have particular susceptibility to all aspects of loss of life. The masses cannot compete at this level of direction and productivity. Complications of long-term stresses with no interaction of spontaneity changes all movement structures in the body, not for its benefit.

## *SPACE-BASED ADAPTATIONS*

All that I do, produce, implement and strive for are movements achieved in opposition to gravity with rotational movements. Remembering the influence of Newton, for every action there is an equal and opposite response to the action. New dynamics that recognize when you offer force, you receive force. However, when you offer rotation, you get rotation. Offering movement-based interplay and exercises that tease the brain to regulate these internal and cognitive processes have to be implemented for long-term space survival. Tasks must include functional locomotion. True human locomotion is the transition of going in and out of movements with momentum. Space-based exercises need to include these transitional interactions rather than repetitive and rote tasks. MARES needs to be relieved of duty and replaced with gyroscopic, interactive movements. Movement, reaction and dynamics within man and all living beings needs to be reexamined with visual perception and mathematical equations.

# Chapter Fifteen

## Getting There Through Gravity

### *Turner's 14th theory of biological gravity*

**A living being's inner rotational fluid dynamics are as important as their movement structure to deliver and sustain the force needed for their living gravity interaction.**

> *"Look up at the stars and not down at your feet. Try to make sense of what you see, and wonder about what makes the universe exist. Be curious."*
>
> – Steven Hawking

The general theory of the effects of gravity on living organisms has been established based on the notion that there is a pull or force that attaches life to the earth. Centrifugal force, a bi-product of earth's rotation, is thought to hold life within the earth's atmosphere. As a ball will fall to the Earth's surface, living organisms are thought to respond in the same manner. This key gravitational force is something that science continues to play with – the data lacks exploration of living organism's play within opposition: nature's key force of gravity.

Newton's first law of motion offers that F=ma (Force = mass x acceleration) as compared to organisms at rest, offering F = m (Force = mass). This equation might be true for simple single cell entities however, a living organism, especially within the animal, amphibian and plant categories are almost never at rest. Within the complexities of the human form, there are countless similarities. However, as there are no two humans that are the same, no two humans share the same movement vocabularies. The development of how they oppose and succumb to gravity are consistently different, individual, and often complex. Even more significant is that the observations are also consistent within all species. Variation of size quickly changes any calculations of movement into that of the ability to use force. Every movement performed is based on previous conversations and calculations of movement and one's ability to manipulate force. Although there are key laws in physics that represent how humans view gravity and the movement within these principles, the human body, having no fixed points in space and being a living organism, discovers complex actions for movement, momentum and acceleration (2). Therefore the calculation of a body's weight subject to gravity, P = mg (P is the weight of the body = mass gravity) is for a reference of amount not ability for movement within gravity.

We can get a glass from the cupboard with very little effort. At the exact same time an inanimate object (mass), such as a brick, having no rotational movements, will immediately fall to the floor. It is true, and I agree, if I were to fall to the floor, I would fall at the same rate as the brick. However, you and I don't walk down the hall with the mental process of 'do not fall'. To perform this task we actually walk through gravity.

We still view gravity as an unknown source that holds life, as we know it, to this planet. Gravity also creates environments that are diverse to every planet in the solar system. Gravity is what holds man together and the system as a whole that surrounds us into infinity. This knowledge has led us to believe that gravity's origin is from a single source. However, every planet and star that we have access to exhibit an equal and different relationship to this source of gravity. We feel the perpetual pull of the sun binding our solar system in movement patterns that are repetitive as a clock that doesn't need to be wound. For this to be true, allow the notion of various sources of gravity within the solar system and beyond that binds all that we know that the universe has to offer. For it is the inner rotational bind in each planet and star creating the binding force we call gravity.

Did you ever stop to think about all of this and realize that we are getting to where we are going with rotation through gravity? I did! Years ago, I was reading a book about Einstein. There was mention of the space shuttle. My children aren't of a generation of the space shuttle so I was describing this great ship on top of rockets. When visualizing the space shuttle taking off, I was remembering its majestic take off. The internal thrust needed with a key backwards spin for its realization of escape velocity was paradigm to how I see, experience, and process movement. Three hours after this experience I jumped from my bed thinking it can't be this simple.

I work with any and all diagnoses involved with special children and adults. It was never about anyone's diagnosis, for Graham, my son, taught me to see the possibilities in everyone. But my wahoo moment was the common denominator – anyone who was special had very little ability to produce or maintain rotational movements. They are given all sorts of visual assessments from hypotonic to hypertonic, mixed tone, spastic and non-responsive. It didn't matter. Not one person was the exception to the rule. In addition, when they were given support to create vertical stability, those too, had no offer for rotation. This combination created force or lack of force. You see with living organisms, when you have force, you get force. When you have movement, you get movement. Synchronized movement needs rotation for structure and integration. I've been developing, teaching and presenting my theories ever since.

Now, as I'm developing new material, I sat down to brush up and learn about all that gravity has to offer. It was so cumbersome due to everyone's wonderful involvement. Suddenly I realized that science has it all wrong. At the same time I realized that I couldn't just call up NASA or Elon and say, "Do you have a moment? You need to change your program." I got a little tired and frustrated with all the great technological advancements, knowing that no one in the space program knew how to get a human being to live a multi-planetary life due to the general lack of knowledge regarding biological responses to gravity. I was crushed when Dr. Tyson presented that we really don't know much about human beings and gravity. If we put this girl on a swing and remove friction, she would swing for infinity. Well, in breathing, digestion, circulation, there is friction, so with that observation, she would die. We are not inanimate objects, our mass is not the same in various places of the universe, and we are not pinned to anything.

I felt like I needed to get all my thoughts down to speed things along. Everyone is so close to the answer and they just need a little help. My hope is that this book creates the push necessary to move the rest of the way to a correct understanding. Realize that just flipping the pages of this book, you are using rotational movements in opposition to gravity. Therefore it is a functional movement. It's the "through gravity" that is the observation. Walking down the hallway is moving through gravity. Swinging on a swing is pumping through gravity. Now in this sense, we are going to need the help of Dr. Feynman, who loved to note his giggly atoms. He liked to describe when I place my hand on the table, I'm not combining or binding with the table, I'm actually floating on the table. There will always be some atoms between myself and the table. If I put chocolate into milk, I now have chocolate milk. I cannot get the chocolate out of the milk to have two separate items ever again. Part of the ease of walking down the hallway is that I'm not combining with the floor. My body knows that I can have an interaction of active and passive muscles organizing through the pelvis for a perpetual force of muscle and movement based interaction that propels us forward.

It's the Earth's rotation that engages our inner molecules in combination with the inner muscle structure. It is widely held that the muscle structure of myosin/actin uses muscles to perform any and all physical tasks, but there has been little discussion as to the invitation of those muscle functions in the human body for form and response.

In contrast to conventional wisdom, advanced movement patterns are not dependent upon the body's muscle structure rather upon its relationship to its inner knowledge of strength and capabilities of lift/load responses, balance, counterbalance and spatial orientation within known surroundings. All movement patterns, including subconscious activities used to organize man within his surrounding, include rotation. It is within the act of rotation that muscles are able to react and efficiently utilize the mass of the skeletal system. Ultimately, the use of rotation allows man to move in and out of simple and complex environments efficiently.

Mature cognitive development varies from increasing new learning practices to enhancing established neuro-pathways to changing and enhancing muscle strength and movement patterns. The ability to maintain physical mobility increases with various forms of physical measurements. Core strength, abdominal muscles and enlarged bicep muscles are desired outcomes for function and anti-aging. In contrast, understanding the human body's natural ability of perpetual motion will increase system mechanic functions. It is movement that combines the actions of momentum and mass through opposition to gravity that will most effectively improve man's locomotion and cognitive function.

Enhanced performance using the techniques of rotation within the skeletal muscles utilizes an explosion of perpetual motion to create a new spin on function and propulsion of the human form.[11] Within the muscle fiber, actin (thin filaments) is thought to slide due to a pulling action of myosin (thick filaments). This paper proposes that when myosin attaches to the cross-bridges, the act itself causes perpetual motion within the cell. The synchronized rotation within the filament during a muscle contraction creates the energy source for opposing two forces in which momentum, movement, acceleration and cognitive manipulation may take place. The creation of a pull onto the muscle fiber produc-

---

11 Perpetual Motion in Human Beings: The Relationship of Movement and Acceleration in Locomotion; Turner, 2016.

es and stores the energy that is needed for the action. The release of this action allows the release of energy into the system mechanics for a controlled reaction and/or action. As we look at the entire human function, as in biped locomotion, the act of balance and counterbalance creates the opposing contraction and release for perpetual motion. The minute action of myosin rotating in coordination with actin can bring upon a coordinated response of energy release or motion in walking. The movement and energy structure is converted, creating a constant and often synchronized use of potential and kinetic energy.

As we change this view of anatomic function to functional anatomy, we begin to see the possibility of myosin and actin moving in a rotational spine to create kinetic energy for perpetual motion. Although it is true that within an action potential of a muscle contraction the size of the muscle will change, a contracted muscle cannot create movement within itself. Additionally, there are many cases where stabilization of the human body, and adding to the dimensions of movement through an exterior stimuli (e.g. walking poles, bicycle), a person with an average or below average advantage to rotational range of motion can sustain greater balance and counter- balance to allow ease and increase of momentum, gait and visual complexities through these devices. A person who finds movement difficult or needs new direction in order to manipulate manual instructions would benefit by including manual rotation and perpetual motion in applied touch to increase the body's ability to rejuvenate interior muscle functions. All implementations of the rotational principles create balance and counterbalance in the movement and the system experiences a new movement which leads to learning.

This new view of the movement within the muscle fiber does not explain general faults within a particular body's functional movement patterns. Most commonly, as we age, the weakness or lack of use of the muscle fiber will change the patterning of the actual center of contraction causing a decrease in synchronized spin within the thick and thin filaments.

It is known that all living organisms organize within the opposition to gravity. The human body walks down the hallway through gravity. For that same body to get out of bed, off the floor, or reach for a cup, these habitual movements are done in a response that is away from this gravitational force. Living systems need various forms of rotation to perform these tasks. Since all responses to stimuli initiate in opposition, the neuro-mapping is computed in a counteraction. The most common action is that of the human eye, as an object is observed then placed in opposition or upside down in cognitive formation. This is the same for the body as we observe a person that has suffered a traumatic brain injury to the right hemisphere, the left side of the body is affected. In actuality, the cognitive formation prior to the stroke creates neural-pathways in opposition to the action. When the TBI occurs, it is the counteractions that lose this awareness to perform tasks due to the trauma's erase or gap in the central nervous system response to all tasks that are affected by that path. In many cases, detours can be introduced through cognitive awareness if the system is able to learn from cause and effect or has mastered a skill through the ability to teach the action. A system that is unable to do either must rely on an outside source to create the stimulus necessary that evokes initiation and enhancement so that the system can create new movement neuro-mapping.

Movement, reaction and dynamics within man and all living beings needs to be reexamined with visual perception and mathematical equations. The significance of this presentation is not only to understand the origin and continuation of perpetual motion but to open the doors to predetermine man's availability to enhance the momentum of muscle function. Research needs to be conducted in typical myosin/actin formation and non-typical cellular presentation, in regard to strength in coordination with function. More importantly, science must document the initiation, stimulation and exercises in developmental movement patterns, health maintenance and aging in the human body. Evidence has been presented that high-powered cycling can decline the effects of the neuro-disorder of Parkinson's. "Researchers have developed an algorithm to control a motor on the bike and used a controller to sense the patient's rate of exertion and adjust the motor based on their input."[12] Future studies examining the importance of cross-referencing momentum specific myosin/actin function in therapy responses are strongly suggested.

Big Bang Theory time. Let's look at muscle function in a new light to examine the cognitive organization of infants as they transition to a more controlled adult manipulation of movement. It is important to note that involuntary muscle functions (ie, cardiac and respiratory) and sub-senses (ie, balance and counterbalance) should remain as a subconscious and automatic response in the nervous system. Skeletal muscles as well as involuntary muscles can be manipulated to become an

---

12 Initiation and stimulation of functional movement and system mechanics. Huggins K & Turner M.; 2016

automatic and deliberate cognitive response depending on the individual's stage of development.

In newborns, the ability to respond to stimuli is critical to cognitive development. This initiation of developmental movement patterns depends on an infant's ability to rotate. A baby's ability to rotate will allow the system to oppose gravity and initiate such movements as reaching, nursing and breathing. During this stage of development, skeletal muscles are not controlled and cannot be controlled with deliberate action. During this stage, a baby has barely engaged its topical senses of sight, sound, touch, hearing and taste. Therefore, the neuromuscular junction, although formed, is not directing specific cognitive responses for a controlled function.

The ebbs and flows of development will engage the infant's system mechanics to begin to exhibit the crude mastering of some skills while simultaneously introducing higher skills of movement, momentum, acceleration and cognitive manipulation. An infant will advance from spasms and random grabbing to crossing midline and holding an object with two hands to playing with two objects all by the time the baby reaches one year of age. The increased successes of interactions with different forces of movement create a hierarchy of developmental movement patterns within the young child. It is within this specific response to stimuli that life becomes fascinating.

When an infant responds to stimuli, various forces are involved. One principle force is created when an object must act upon another. This type of force can be initiated, manipulated and mastered in the body as one ages to adulthood. A body in its infancy is unable to perform any of these actions or responses. The development of complex movements begins in infancy and builds upon the exploration of limb movement, followed by trunk involvement and ultimately whole body movements. Therefore, in order to understand human movement and cognitive development, there must be further analysis of the stages of development within the principles of movement. By reevaluating developmental movement patterns in babies during their early stages, I discovered that for any system to respond to stimuli and create a cognitive response, the act of rotation must be present in all initial movements.

The patterning in an infant's system mechanics initiates around the opposition of gravity for the development of functional movement. Any initiation of purposeful movement in an infant creates interruptions with typical milestone achievement. If a baby appears to exhibit the ability to lift rather than transfer weight, its system is at serious risk for developmental delays. Present scientific theories of applied force imply that it is the presence of force that moves the body and influences movement while cognitive scientists have typically employed theory-based tests in an attempt to isolate and evaluate how various factors influence brain structures and mental processes. However, the arguments exhibited in these theories are often based upon adult movement functions. This view implies that human function is maintained by muscle function. It must be recognized that force may influence how an individual moves but it does not influence how an individual moves due to force. A baby cannot initiate purposeful or controlled muscle function. Muscles are involved in reacting and responding to stimuli, but it is the interaction of the human body's system mechanics with the opposition to gravity that is responsible for neuro-typical movement. Therefore, in newborns, the ability to respond to stimuli is the key to cognitive development.

In children, the advances in gross-motor skills allow them to begin to challenge the forces of nature. When a child's system learns to ride and interact with a bicycle, several factors need to be present in their bodies. Balance, counterbalance and spatial orientation in combination with controlled muscle functions are needed to synchronize movement within a visually complex environment. A child that presents with difficulties in biped locomotion, such as walking and running, are bound to have challenges when riding a bicycle. A child that exhibits challenges with balance and counterbalance within their surroundings will not be able to then manipulate those forces through an external object. The skeletal muscles function best within the immature development of a child's mind and system mechanics. It is when a motion interacts within these two processes that endless skipping, rolling and playing results. The recognition of a body's ability to tap into the source of perpetual motion is not only enjoyable but can be developed into higher functions of skill and achievement. More significantly, it can be integrated to a place of graceful aging rather than regression.

In adults, the formed cognitive response to stimuli is processed in a filing system in the brain and the desire to initiate new movements into the system mechanics typically diminishes with age. Adults will have also formed opinions and potential outcomes of how most movements are to be performed by them and by those around them. When a developed brain is challenged to a new learning opportunity, it will predetermine a pattern or group of steps that need to be achieved for this new process to occur. In addition, the brain will establish a time limit for lack of achievement within one or more of the proposed goals. The standards for continued development of the matured brain cannot be mirrored in an infant or child. It is also within these differences that perpetual movement, momentum, acceleration and cognitive manipulation begin to stagnate and/or diminish. In the adult mind, the cognitive process will base many decisions for growth and development on past performance and character development rather than with a playful sense of wonder.

Movement is the key to all functions of life as we know it. Stimulating functional movement and rotation within the human body rather than associating strength for accomplished lifting actions can improve the cognitive processing dynamics. Additional research is needed to show the interplay of muscle function and cognitive function in developmental milestone achievements.

# POP QUIZ:

**Question #9: What new calculations can you find for measuring an athlete's rotation in ratio with their escape velocity within their mass/might dynamics.**

## *SPACE-BASED COMPLICATIONS*

Man's muscular force depends on the ratio of maximum speed needed to perform an action under normal gravitational conditions. In actuality, all gravitational conditions are normal to a man's nervous system, however it is the other sub-sense's experience that can cause issues with typical mass/might calculations. A person's sensitivity to temperature can cause a deviation in their ability to reach previously achieved measurements of force, speed and dexterity.

To date, dominant physiological limits are more noted than any evaluation of the functional integration of that person's developmental movement patterns. The simple examination of rotation throughout the body is a simple and clear indicator of ability for prior and present tasks at hand and continuing cognitive growth. Any and all movements in human beings are learned without controlled muscle function. The ability to respond to stimuli is with rotation and random movements which are slowly added, developed and eventually controlled.

The consideration of man's ability to move through weakness is more accurately exhibited in areas of noted aptitudes of strength. As with man's weakness needing exterior care in nutrition, housing and medical provisions, those aspects are encroaching on his abilities without knowing his true existence. The not knowing of self or wanting to do better or what has been considered great also are needing assistance of nutrition, housing and medical provisions. The controlled use of gyms, training camps and enhancing manipulations of drugs and/or surgery for the sake of force and force alone is unnatural for human potential. The ability to lift 456 kg is not essential for cognitive development or enhancing the family or society. It is within the lack of true calculations that man and machine are getting lost and away from survival and growth initiative.

Mankind needs to take a step back from its definitions of the general laws of biology of size and its control of mass. Not only can an ant carry a load greater than its own body weight, but it has no muscle mass. At the same time, an elephant's organization and constitution is not to carry loads; that has been man's effort to use the elephant for human gains. An ant who tunnels into the earth with other species opening up water access into the earth is overlooked, but is just as significant as a man who needs to labor for increase and development of housing and goods, or an elephant that can provide natural transport. Man's ability to lift a weight is not necessary or critical for its survival; however, with little need for manual labor and abundant free time, there is a constant desire to find the ultimate force within mankind.

## *SPACE-BASED ADAPTATIONS*

Taking humans from the context of movement that he knows as formulas not strength, as in long-term space travel, is not just noted in muscle mass. As our brain goes back into a womb-like existence, the only period in the organism's time that there was no formal opposition to gravity, it brings our being to that of non-muscle necessity not that of muscle atrophy. It is true that muscle composition and capacity diminish; however, those are the most obvious observations. Our cognitive awareness with no achievable developmental milestones, i.e. when you cannot stand, walk or crawl, without the opposed gravity and forces within your being and system mechanic functions. It is the introduction of these forces in controlled exercises that will aid in the precedence of the muscles needed for a more functional return back to the stimulus that earth's gravity provides.

There can be situations where there is a noticeable improvement in force, speed, and manipulations. However, inappropriate measures, as seen with dehydration and drug manipulations, can also cause frailties within the system mechanics. The erroneous conclusion that a decrease in mass increases propulsion as seen in objects regarding velocity are a different science than movement in human dynamics.

The observation that the American astronauts can more easily manipulate their movements on the lunar surface under the assumption of a lowered or lunar gravity is comparing apples to oranges. Man also suddenly knew to jump-skip around using cognitive manipulations of locomotion rather than to run and walk. The simple act of bending over and picking up a stone needs to be replaced with equipment manipulation since the opposition of two forces and non-lunar rotation prevent the act of bending over. The new wealth of knowledge that the effects of gravity on the human body, based on movement calculations within the opposition to gravity, to further manipulate mass and acceleration to increase capacity while maintaining strength needed for an earth based existence.

New devices and measurements can not only aid various sizes of humans to achieve tasks that were thought to be impossible based on a strength based ecosystem, but within these protocols, humans that were thought to have cognitive but not a physical stature can create tasks and even outperform those with muscle stamina. Individuals with observable high levels of absolute strength cannot necessarily achieve levels of mass based calculations without the experience or intuitive sense to work with both protocols of gravity. They have the ability to force movement rather than to manipulate and calculate movement in environments that include new and different external forces.

We can come to the following conclusions: every living organism on earth functions based on its ability to oppose and move in, around, and through the known gravitational force. It is not a gravitational immunity, but rather a learned knowledge that acceleration through locomotion continues without the concern for falling or lack of accomplishment. Within that context, the use of force or known muscle function, that supersedes functional movement, instead creates a decreased strength and ability to perform the task at hand. Since man has an errant understanding of how gravity works, how we work within gravity creates a disadvantage compared to other living organisms. The ease with which a monkey runs from the ground to a tree, across a roof to another tree is seamless without any necessary or conscious observation of how to do it or fear of failure. Their ability to manipulate within space is true to their form and only their form. This is found from species to species. With humans there is also the effect of cognitive influence. Our concern with how we will perform within an artificial concept of normal strength and speed leads to failures within those boundaries, personal and/or professional.

# Chapter Sixteen
# We All Float Differently

## *Turner's 15th theory of biological gravity*

**Living buoyancy must be at or within the same relationship with living rotational movement.**

> *"Gravitation is, so far, not understandable in terms of other phenomena."*
>
> – Richard P. Feynman

A basketball will float on top of the water or the floor of the earth's surface, not the bottom. If I try to push the basketball under water, it will return to that surface at the same perpendicular force as the perpendicular fall to the surface from above. Depending on the amount of inner air between the force of the water and outer atmosphere, it allows the ball to return to the surface. When a human is compromised, they fall to the ground. That same person when gasping for air, in or out of water, will automatically go up for air. The human body's reflexes are actually gravitationally based for our functional movements.

A human body will also float on the surface. But when a body is drowning, and succumbs to death, it automatically sinks or falls to the ground in the water. Therefore, there are living buoyancy principles that organize to oppose gravity versus succumbing to gravity.

"Oxygen is the lifeblood of living organisms," said Dr. George Daley, dean of Harvard Medical School. "Without oxygen, cells can't survive." But too much or too little oxygen also can be deadly.[13] The three researchers (William G. Kaelen, Jr., Sir Peter J. Ratcliffe, and Gregg L. Semenza) tried to answer this question: How do cells regulate their responses?

Cells regulate or respond to an inner ability to create and regulate rotational movement and momentum through many organizations, the most prominent of which is myosin and actin. The body's ability to reg-

13 Nobel Prize in Medicine Awarded for Research on How Cells Manage Oxygen, NY Times, 10/07/2019

ulate oxygen is not only a key component for life, but for buoyancy as well. This is another remarkable aspect of our body's creating, interacting with and moving through gravity. It involves interaction at a cellular level with components of buoyancy interaction, not only through oxygen regulation, but within the pressure created by the body's responses to stimulus and movement of inner biological rotations, not by muscle contraction.

A baby drawing their first breath is regulating its ability to oppose gravity based on its inner buoyancy or draw. Any infant that is compromised during this phase will have difficulties in vertical milestones. This is due to the fact that if they cannot regulate gravity for breathing in a horizontal position, they will be unable to do so interacting in upright positions.

In addition, any infant that is unable to consistently cycle a full breath during this period will also be muscularly impaired. The buoyancy that is observed in the lungs is actually going through the mechanics of the whole body to incorporate the milestone of breathing at a unique cellular level.

There is a specific relationship to the horizontal, vertical and transitional movements needed to develop and interact with these aspects of force and movement. We float above the surface of water, as we do below. We must also note that our feet are not pinned to the ground. An aspect of gravity that needs to be brought out with all of these interchangeable dynamics of how we, as humans, are able to continue to use the inner mechanics of coming to the surface.

Let us take a look at the simple interaction of getting out of bed. "Rise and shine", your mother once called to you. Even she knew there was a secret hidden within your daily, functional movements. This is because we call on a simple, yet highly complex, aspect of buoyancy in a gravitational reference for that specific human being. This is part of the reason that you can't just evaluate reflexes in global evaluation techniques for children and adults with special circumstances. The skeletal system is the primary response needed to connect this crucial central counter response through fascia, muscle, and organs for tension, viscosity and gravitational interaction. Therefore, a simple inner response of what might be referred to as a head lift or core strength needed to get us out of bed, the crucial first bounce interrelated with rotational response creates a movement, from within the bone, to rise up or practically float into a sitting position. Simple acts of weight shifting are made optimal using the buoyancy-based approach rather than through specific muscle-based, static interactions. Compared to an adult, a teenager is better able to manipulate these crude movements, but they are based off of the brain's ability to copy or mimic a movement rather than an organic response of personal interaction that enhances all cognitive skills.

Creating scenarios, repeating or patterning techniques, which can be observed in therapies and load/lift interactions, allow the body to have an attempt for achievement rather than the knowing of accomplishment. If a system has not been able to exhibit initiation skills that include rotational movements, it will present with special needs at some level.

From the moment a baby is born, a typical infant needs to interact with these first sensations that go through the body. Key abilities of finding neutral, an absolute horizon and the interaction of buoyancy tension initiates through the spinal column and quickly goes into all bone matter, are all achieved by interacting with these sensations. Articulation occurs through the interaction of gravitational reflexes during the first few months. Deviations due to environmental influences, or even system trauma, quickly fail the body and lead to a movement interaction that is similar to a simple mass-based interaction. This is where Newton's law comes into play and the nervous system is now interacting to succumbing to gravity rather than opposing.

This is a key principle for astronauts. This is a perfect moment to take "fall" out of the conversation. A baby needs to learn how to fall. An astronaut, who thinks falling can be an issue to a life event, no longer knows how to fall. However, their mechanics of living buoyancy are immediately removed from the nervous system, especially throughout all skeletal processes. The sensation of rising now supersedes the ratio such that it is too significant to offer rotational movements for any functional movement to occur. All cognitive formatting for any and all developmental milestones cease to exist the moment they leave the earth's pull ratio needed for human dynamics. It's not the lack of gravity that will eventually kill a human being; it is the increase of living buoyancy while lacking any rotational movements that completely changes the inner dynamics of the human body, creating a type of special needs.

In this field of developmental movement patterns, the body is now succumbing to the float, the opposite of succumbing to gravity, but the mental failure is still the same. The immediate side-effect of this is the space station form of autism: unable to play well with others and immediate loss of all developmental movement patterns, where the body goes into failure.

Living buoyancy is one of the key laws to living organisms. The other aspect is that the human body can organize these principles in any angle. It doesn't need a gravitational floor as a reference point. The absolute horizon is not some distant visual field; it is a systemic organization embedded inside our bodies from infancy. We don't fully integrate those principles until we hit our spinning milestones between the ages of 2.5 to 5 years of age. From there come interactions of somersaults, actual spinning - creating a visual nystagmus, rolling down a hill, merry-go-rounds, swimming, swinging, to cartwheels and bicycle riding. These are crucial gravity-based interactions that are needed for the human body and brain to advance into master's level of global achievements. However, it is important to note that, as technology advances into the lives of younger and younger children, and the lack of recognition of this developmental period grows, placing the body's ability to oppose gravity with rotational movements into all aspects of the nervous system, the failure to thrive is happening at a much more global rate. One in six children in the United States alone receives supplemental services needed to help with speech, social interaction and movement locomotion.

We are and have been doing this to astronauts for the past 60 years. The act of spinning in space is a visual satisfaction based on no reference to how the body can move. As an astronaut spins around in space, the only sensation that they have to this act is visual feedback from the environment. Their bodies are unable to oppose gravity, exhibit rotational movement, process key core movements or transitional skills, or feel any force of movement. They are therefore unable to regulate internal buoyancy that the mind and body know and recognize as a life force. Thus, the expansion of their body starts to rip it apart from a cellular and systemic level.

Just to note, you are starting to understand that under no circumstance do these functional movements include the interaction of centrifugal force. Few sports - surfing, skiing, skateboarding, and some aspects of bicycle riding - are able to offer that sensation to the human body. Once the human brain transfers the ability to perform transitional milestones through those aspects of movement, the brain deviates to a form of autistic traits, with antisocial behavior, isolating from gravity-based humans, being unable to work to the same capacity as before, changes in speech patterns and stress related problem solving skills being just a few of the related symptoms. This is due to the downward pull motion, pinning the feet to the object. Rarer cases include those that need the sensation of falling ratios, found in skydiving and base jumping; however, these sports have similar psychological effects to the brain and body. I will note that this may be confusing to some because we are commonly taught that muscle-based responses are the ultimate human achievement. Those that are able to do those tasks have stamina and are able to perform with very agile movements. We need to stop viewing performance and action-based achievements as healthy.

## *SPACE-BASED COMPLICATIONS*

Spinning the space station will do as much damage, if not more, than the lack of gravity living in space provides. "What's up, dude," is not what Houston wants to hear, but organizing the body to a downward pull is not the same as the force of gravity. In a human body, gravity is not necessarily a pull, but a binding force interaction that is necessary for all of our cognitive and physical development.

## *SPACE-BASED ADAPTATIONS*

The sciences need to realize there is no activity based on the organization of functional movements that includes a pinning force to the feet or any other area of the body. We can easily roll around in bed as we sleep, not due to pure muscle calculations, but because we can. This is gravity interaction at its purest. Don't believe me? Have you had an operation lately? Was it almost impossible to get out of bed? Medications are required to put you out, which diminish your internal use of rotational movements. For most people, as the medication leaves the body during the next week, their skills slowly start to improve. A hospital will let you go home when you can walk up and down a hallway. To most, strength is the key component for these tasks. An astronaut, similar to getting out of surgery, finds themself not being able to 'walk down the hallway'. These are the kinds of simulations that astronauts need on a daily basis, throughout the day - not on a treadmill, but in expansion equipment suitable for their needs.

# Chapter Seventeen
## Out of the Womb

### *Turner's 16th theory of biological gravity*

**Living beings develop in fluid dynamics without opposing gravity to create a being through the mode of expansion of force. There are no rotational movements during this process. There are no oppositional forces during this time.**

> *"It is paradoxical, yet true, to say, that the more we know, the more ignorant we become in the absolute sense, for it is only through enlightenment that we become conscious of our limitations. Precisely one of the most gratifying results of intellectual evolution is the continuous opening up of new and greater prospects."*
>
> – Nikola Tesla

The development of mammals before birth happens in the womb. During this time, the mother creates a certain ratio of amniotic fluids that interact with her body, setting up the dynamics of a frictionless environment so the fetus can develop equally in all directions. There is gravity present during this time; however, certain key factors cannot participate for full gravitational laws through the eyes of Newton. For instance, there is no scenario where the fetus can fall, as the theories of buoyancy create a systematic rise in a non-cellular environment. Typically, our cells function in fluid interaction, yet they regulate oxygen intake. During the housing in the womb, this natural law is not possible for independent living. It is true that there is a chance of little to no organ functionality within the context of a premature delivery. The lack of cellular structure is one of the greatest risks for an infant during that critical period. This is why current scientific principles are unable to measure actual gravitational force in that developing system. A fetus is unable to create functional movements while in expansion mode. It is also unable to perform system-based movements through expansion and elimination. It is unable to breathe, eat, or eliminate waste while in the womb. At no other time is life exposed to those conditions.

What is the current exception to this? Living in outer space! In the space station, we still have breathing, eating and eliminating. Those are created in an environment where, if it weren't for the ISS, man and all living organisms would perish. Without compression and oppositional force to this compression, the body fails in either environment. The neurological complexities when keeping the body directly in expansion mode are identical to those exhibited within the womb. A gravitational force to a living being outside of the womb is not just a compressive force. It is the interaction of our system mechanics, not biomechanics, that is needed for form and function. Teasing the system through daily interaction with oppositional force and rotational, developmental movements is a necessity in order to take the brain out of being in a "womb environment".

Note that the amniotic fluid and umbilical cord inhibit any action or counter action that include rotation. Similar space-based techniques include foot line tethering inside and outside the station. This technique will have additional impact for bone loss. Similarly, these concepts are also misunderstood in cerebral palsy. It is thought that the pressure from standing is all that is needed to save the hips. Equipment is developed to offer this environment to save the hips and bone density. In reality, however, it is the up and down motion interacting with gravity for optimal health that can actually save the hips and bone density. Otherwise, adults aging wouldn't experience bone loss. Imagine that you need to stack a bunch of boxes. You rotate over to the right from a downward motion to pick up the box. You then complete the rotation and place the box up high. This is a great example of functional movement with rotation. It's not age, but affluence, that is creating a deterioration of these key movements. The more money someone has, the first movements that decrease are those above the shoulders, as they don't prune out trees, bail hay, hang rugs or hang laundry to dry. As humans, we do very little movement with our hands over our heads. Now we are passing these activities, along with their lack of functional movement, to our children. These simple principles can detect the responses for autism, cerebral palsy and genetics. This movement is absolutely impossible for an astronaut to do after he arrives back to earth after a long-term space assignment. It goes back to the simple principle: to oppose gravity, you need rotational movement. When you take away those sensations or the ability to initiate those movements, the result will always be inabilities, pain and special needs. You have automatic muscle and bone loss. These atrophies are not about being in outer space, but the lack of functional movement. In these situations, muscle and bone mass are no longer needed for cognitive function and the system or body deteriorates.

## SPACE-BASED COMPLICATIONS

The only time the body develops in expansion mode is in the womb and within fluid dynamics. When the body is put into outer space, the neurological response is to go into expansion mode. Therefore, you need to offer the body movements based off of the body's neurological responses for functional movement rather than static, linear exercising. The way exercise and most movements are designed for life in space are similar to womb movements, such as running and lifting as if it was a baby kicking and stretching in the womb. The neurological changes to an astronaut's nervous system are immediate and eventually will be life threatening. Previous studies of astronauts have linked spaceflight to muscle atrophy, especially of the muscles that maintain posture and stability while upright on Earth in normal gravity. Many astronauts experience low back pain during and immediately after space missions, and they appear to be at increased risk of spinal disc herniation.[14] Research shows that astronauts have a 21.4 times higher risk for cervical disc herniation than the general population. This is likely due to the mechanical stress on the body from the force of spaceflight, as well as possibly disc expansion and the result of bone mineral loss that occurs in a zero-gravity environment, Dr. Menger and his colleagues explained.[15] Combining friction within a frictionless environment is not a structure that our current cognitive system can adapt to without integration.

## SPACE-BASED ADAPTATIONS

Exercise equipment needs to be adapted to offer the body the ability to respond to primitive stresses. The entire duration of travel without gravity offers no friction within the interior mechanics and exterior responses of the body. Even simple equipment designed for bladder/colon functions needs to be developed to engage the necessary movements that only happen through the process of primitive stress, not fric-

14 Long-duration space missions have lasting effects on spinal muscles, Wolters Kluwer Health, January, 2019

15 How Disc Herniation Changed the History of the Apollo 11 Spaceflight, Kristin Della Volpe, August 2019

tion. Gravity offers the sense of this process through the pull of mass against our opposing responses. It is necessary to create push/pull interactions. These can range from a friendly game of tug-o-war to a system that mimics bailing hay and pruning. This can be accomplished through cables and bungies and provides a simple yet fascinating way to ensure the organization of the body within and around functional movements. Manipulations can include visual organization and depth perception. As a result, an astronaut's first tasks of balance achievements, upon their return to Earth, can be satisfied through visual response rather than solely relying on muscle building and strength output.

# Chapter Eighteen

## Movement Doesn't Fall

### *Turner's 17th theory of biological gravity*

**A living organism will not just fall down like a board, but will instead have variations of the response through rotation and lack of rotation with factors of buoyancy that can counter the force of gravity in living beings.**

> *"First they ignore you, then they laugh at you, then they fight you, then you win."*
>
> – Nikola Tesla

You can flush a toilet, and depending on where those water molecules reside, the water will not fall into the drain in a straight manner, but they will instead rotate as they succumb to gravity or the force of the flush.

## POP QUIZ:

**Question #10: Can you breathe through your nose without your mouth moving?**

I was intrigued by inner rotational movements through Viktor Schrauberger's work with water vortexes. He moved logs down a canal using internal rotational movements for force and momentum; from there, I was able to visualize that with assisted breathing. I've known for a long time that almost all my clients with Chronic Oxygen Pulmonary Disease (COPD) have had major dental work. I find it interesting to see if the palate or soft tissue functions. When there is stress on the system, I look at the lack of movement to find out where the body's movement principles break down.

A ball is buoyant because there's air in it, but there's no interaction. Humans interact within all 360 degrees. A person's level of buoyancy is already at a higher level with every additional functional movement. Lots of experiences with buoyancy, as well as responding to stimuli, forms a very well-trained brain.

And those are the two principles that you lose in outer space. That's why an astronaut comes back to earth like a paperweight.

To conclude, including buoyancy in developmental pediatric, athletic, and professional evaluations, would provide a clearer idea of the development of the child to the physical adult responses, creating the standard model of gravity.

## *SPACE-BASED COMPLICATIONS*

It is thought that when in orbit, you are not floating due to lack of gravity but in a free fall and are weightless. If this was neurologically true, the condition known as falling would create a sensation in our body to stop or prevent the fall. No person knowingly falls as a daily interaction of life events. Living organisms must exhibit rotation throughout their system for any and all displays of force and movement. They initiate and therefore learn from the stimulus of movement within their ability to oppose gravity. The system that cannot naturally move in and out of rotation is guaranteed to fail to exhibit the controlled cognitive movements as in sitting, crawling and jumping or other deemed measurements of force. The observations of animal behaviors are more accurate due to species progression. The measurements of human beings are false due to the prior calculations of what is considered healthy or strong by the creator or evaluator of the initiative.

The common practice is to offer man static exercises or slow movements rather than functional movements. Functional movements enhance our ability to oppose gravity and create and enhance the opposition of forces. This offers stability, growth and strength for everyone from newborns to those that are late in the aging process. It is within man's ability to balance and counterbalance that creates the ability to move within their surroundings. Pure strength will never truly get man anywhere. It is an isolated measurement and not an indicator for longevity and agility.

Note that all living organisms with or without cognitive awareness oppose the force of gravity. This natural phenomenon is constant but not absolute. Therefore the calculations of force due requires mass, which is considered muscle based. Realizing that any and all developmental movement patterns are organized around the organism's ability to oppose gravity, new calculations need to be considered for functional movement. The first task is to calculate the various degrees and acknowledge that man and many animal groups use simple and complex movement equations that include rotation.

## *SPACE-BASED ADAPTATIONS*

Introducing falling or pinning into the ISS is not the solution to the need for gravity. There needs to be recognition of the rotational organization of our use and structure of movement within core movement strategies of living beings. Within the complexities of human form there are countless similarities; however, because every human is unique, we do not share the exact same movements in our response to force. Every movement performed is based on previous calculations of movement and one's ability to manipulate force. Although there are key laws in physics that represent how humans view gravity and movement within these principles, the author's theories, as detailed in this book, demonstrate that these laws are obsolete to human movement. Since a human body does not have any fixed points in space and because it is a living organism, it develops uniquely to discover complex actions for movement, momentum and acceleration.[16] Therefore, the calculation of a body's weight subject to gravity, $P = mg$ (P is the weight of the body = mass gravity) is a reference of amount and not of ability to move within gravity. Weight cannot be viewed as a force or a constant, otherwise all of us could jump over a wall, climb a rope, or run up a flight of stairs with the same finesse. This is not the case. We only see this kind of similarity in simple examples of copying and applied behavioral movements which we currently use for testing range of motion or physical accompaniments.

This is not the case. We only see this kind of similarity in simple examples of copying and applied behavioral movements which we currently use for testing range of motion or physical accompaniments.

The developmental ways that living organisms oppose and succumb to gravity are consistently diverse, individual and often complex. Additionally, the variation of size needs to be an integral part of the calculation of movement as it is applied to an expanded scientific theory on gravitational force or it will not account for dynamic mechanisms involved in creating motion within a living organism.

---

16 The Effect of Gravity on the Development of Living Organisms and Their Strength, Kanyevsky 2014

# PART V
# What Happens When The System Fails Gravity

# Chapter Nineteen
## Bigger is Not Always Better

### *Turner's 18th theory of biological gravity*

**In living beings, when the mass supersedes the might, the mass will prevail.**

> *"Life is 10% what happens to you and 90% how you react to it."*
>
> – Charles R. Swindoll

The architecture of movement is crucial to all that we are. On Earth, as it is in space, we are designed to believe we need the sun, water and oxygen to survive as a species. Exploration has begun to look beyond what we can see to find another source of these energies to sustain us. At the same time, there are currently no considerations of the rotational movements, the core of our beings, to offer the ability to take advantage of the needed internal and external interaction of biology. "The survival of the fittest" is the biggest misconception of our life organization. It has come from the past and into current space programs.

The current school of thought is that muscles and core strength are the key ingredients for our evolution. Or more importantly, they guarantee a spot on the next rocket. Do you have what it takes to defy gravity? Actually, you don't need to have accumulated muscle mass for any action. It is true that there are muscles involved with locomotion, but increased muscle mass does not directly equate to increased mobility.

Let's look at cerebral palsy (CP). On a daily basis, I try to help those with brain trauma due to premature deliveries, birth injuries, or accidents. At this stage, there are various ways of approaching movement as goals. The most typical achievement is a milestone, a static pose of an action needed for a child to proceed to the next level. Another approach is the prevention of a system response that needs to be avoided, most likely due to spasticity or failed reflex integration. I also need to direct those coming to me to fix something or help a child to be more typical. Usually they fail to realize the unique approach to movement responses due to structure or knowledge of a core action response.

The same issues can be true for our current space protocols, from preparations to facilitations. Specific movement goals have been set for the group as a whole through maintaining inner body functions through exterior actions. More importantly, NASA and other agencies have very specific lists of body deviations to be avoided at all costs. Any deviations from the set norms of the present program need to be corrected at all costs. The bodies of astronauts are continuing to fail under this model just as children with CP.

Why would we have these clear similarities between astronauts and a form of special needs? The clear answer is here in the eighteenth law of movement: in living beings, when the mass supersedes the might, the mass will prevail. Whether you are a person with CP, an astronaut, or somewhere in between, we all complete a series of movements where a form of might is needed to produce, involve, and/or complete a task. Progressive assertion comes into play as we move through life. Whether it is a physical or emotional achievement, exertion comes into play. However, one must realize that a task needs none of this to come to fruition. Sure, lifting 500 pounds will need a bit of strength from our bodies. If we do this on a regular basis, we might try to trick the body into thinking that this is a functional movement. Failing to realize that our bodies will not be able to maintain this will instantly result in atrophy due to loss of upkeep or practice. This could happen today or years from now, but at some point, the mass will supersede the might. Rockets have exploded due to the miscalculations of a rotational exit from the Earth and the mass of the atmosphere dominates the might of the fuel, crushing it into combustion. A child with CP, when shown a form of walking that does not involve rotational movements in opposition of gravity, will most likely fail to continue to walk between the ages of ten and sixteen. This is due to a mass increase going beyond the might of the child. In most cases, a child will have pneumonia or surgery, something that may subtly change the might of their being, and just like that, will no longer be able to achieve the movement of a week prior. This is no different than an astronaut attempting to return to earth and suddenly having no ability to eat or move. This is not due to the force of gravity. A person is unable to move in and out of positions due to their inability to organize in and around the gravitational bind. In both situations, it is the lack or inability to oppose gravity with rotational movements. Therefore, their bodies only know how to accomplish actions through might to mass ratios.

Neither scenario is due to muscle loss but is instead due to movement loss or lack of innovation.

Let's look at how movement organization is created. Before a baby is delivered, none of these movements are present. The baby needs to be able to leave their mother without getting 'stuck' in the vaginal canal. The perfect environment for fetal development is one without friction in order for the body to form properly in all directions as it grows or expands in size for full development. Note that any baby who experiences friction in the womb has complications with dimorphic features and possible delays. Throughout fetal development, it presents with no individual bone articulation. Another significant factor to note is that during the time in the womb, there is no true gravity to create a counter movement due to the amniotic fluid and lack of eliminations in the baby's body from breathing or digestion.

As soon as the baby is born, they are meant to be able to experience gravity and find the floor. They then experience counter-movements through the pelvis as the movement quickly synchronizes throughout its body. This is also our first neutral state for our spine's nervous system. The spine is the dominant point for organization that all skeletal responses interact with. These crucial movements during our first days of life are requirements for all infant development presentation to any and all future life skills.

It is within this countering that all of the bones are set up for independent movements throughout the human body. Compressions and other restrictions due to medical and/or environmental situations will affect all movements. If this happens, the complexities needed to twist will not present without intervention. The earlier the child can be stimulated, the more likely it will gain the necessary skills needed to transition from sitting to all fours and upper quadrant vision.

Let us compare the first few days of life to an astronaut's initial space experience. The first key similarities are the body's response to minimum gravity. The immediate sensation of gravity leaving the body equally takes away a body's ability to respond to stimuli with rotational movements. Equally, the ability for bone articulation becomes static and linear, similar to the nervous system's inability in the womb to establish any counter-movements. Most people believe that it is the lack of gravity's presence on the human body that initiates the body's growth. A factor that needs to be addressed is that this experience switches the body's system mechanics back to the expansion mode experienced in the womb: the body's ability to expand, in all directions, in a frictionless environment.

# POP QUIZ:

**Question #11: Calculate the rotation and gravitational assessment of humans prior to their space experience to predict their ability or inability for buoyancy organization.**

## *SPACE-BASED COMPLICATIONS*

The severe reduction of gravity and rotation for an astronaut increases the body's buoyancy and establishes their new ability to float. The new movement equation needed is the amount of each body's internal and neurological interactions. From that we can begin to implement the movement principles needed to counter the lack of rotation within opposition to gravity into their daily routines. This is a mandatory change needed if we expect multi-planetary colonies and long-term space travel to be in our future. Equally so, stimulations should be experienced, not to create a false gravity, but to introduce biological movements for an astronaut's nervous system to experience the floor as it relates to their body. Our body's neutral relationship to all established internal and external movements organizes around an absolute horizon. The elimination and/or removal of gravity is noted in the astronaut's bodies, and is most visible in their inability to sleep or perform any of our developmental milestones or movement patterns.

A baby, beginning to interact with a ball or rattle, is organizing the weight of the ball through the counter of the pelvis. Imagine a system so sensitive that, when mass is placed on or inserted into the body, all movements respond around the mass. If I were to work on you, allowing you to feel a certain achievement of core movement transfer, then lay your cell phone on one area of your body, this phenomenon will either alter or cease to exist altogether. It's not the weight of the cell phone, but its mass equates to movement deviations through the recipient. This is why a baby that grabs an object but is unable to release can no longer counter and will not be able to cross midline or transition into a vertical milestone. It's one of the earliest signs of cerebral palsy (hypertonic). They will develop with a stiff response. A baby that can't interact or is prevented from these interactions (hypotonia) will also not be able to counter, to cross midline, or transition into vertical. They will develop with a floppy response.

The most significant neurological loss is any and all progressive system stresses of interactions of mass and might. Every movement turns into tasks of mimic and copying, a process that requires thought rather than counter-interactions. This initiates the complex and complete removal of the body's response to the natural principles of movement. Similar to formatting a hard drive, the body, having no functional movements, immediately loses all internal organization. When the body has no opposition to gravity with rotational movement, the muscles are equally unresponsive and leave the system. Being unable to experience a mass/might ratio increases the inability to return to earth. Re-entry to the gravitational bind removes all buoyancy which equally influences the lack of counteraction, making these movement ratios incapable of producing rotational movements. This process creates an abnormal over-response to the gravitational bind. At the same time, all other body movements are now synchronizing around this interaction. It is imperative that any and all post space flight rehabilitation is revised to incorporate these new body calculations. Protocols need to reflect the individual's response, or more specifically lack of response, to perform oppositional rotational actions within the nervous system's definition of functional movements. Failure to do so prolongs or potentially eliminates the ability of that person's body to return to essential interactions of gravity, rotation and buoyancy from a cellular to systematic response. The more efficient this equation is, the easier it is for the body to organize through weight transfer and stamina versus mass and might.

Tumors and certain other infections do not present within the living gravitational organization, but to that of the mass instead. This is why the apple fell to the ground. In an apple, when the mass supersedes the movements, it will fall to the earth. While the apple utilizes the rotational and buoyancy movements of the tree, it will stay within the tree's colony. At the exact moment when this equation differs, it will be unable to continue this relationship with the tree and falls to the ground.

This is one of the key reasons why a cold is much more difficult for an astronaut. The difference in internal mass is the complete opposite in space as it is on the ground. Let's look at a sneeze. On the ground, the mass/might ratio is engaged, and a sneeze is propelled forward. However, a person with special needs instead propels backwards. In space, there are no mass/might ratios engaged. Not only does an astronaut propel in opposition to the trajectory of the sneeze, they might need to hold onto something, otherwise, they can fly into something.

On the ground, the human body goes in and out from a being, that is, opposing gravity through rotation to succumbing to gravity with lack of rotation. One of the reasons that a person can die with very little cancer is due to this internal phenomenon. When a person's organization succumbs to gravity and it hits their internal rotations, the lack of rotation alone is enough to stop the body from its being. In outer space, you have a being that is neither opposing nor succumbing to gravity. When non-rotational internal movements hit an astronaut through an internal mass, it's their buoyancy manipulation that is now thrown. Their internal and external float is now involved with an abnormal reference point, similar to their experience when first manipulating a weightless environment.

Bringing an astronaut back to earth with no ability to calculate a healthy mass/might ratio will cause post-space complications for the rest of their life. Agony and pain should not be a daily resistance. It's inhumane and unacceptable.

## *SPACE-BASED ADAPTATIONS*

As we mature, we learn to manipulate and organize our movements for action, attainment and completion. New mathematical equations are needed in order to establish daily tasks derived from functional movements in healthy neuro-typical mass/might ratios calculated for the specific individual. Note that it is based on of a specific individual's organization of mass including buoyancy and rotation, therefore, mass is not a constant on an internal basis or as a group or herd. As movement is a personal experience, the calculations of every movement would be based on the internal complexities that can change hourly. For instance, the type of sleep can alter these calculations. Understanding those ratios would also change space-based sleep programs. Again, let us note that sleep medications are overused in outer space. These medications change internal rotation dynamics or slow them down. Adaptations in movement interactions, or exercises, need to include push/pull activities found in most sports.

This introduction of system mechanics and its relationship to the principles of movement creates a new mathematical approach to identifying man's movement patterns and relationship with the opposition to gravity. Human beings are constantly bombarded with the possibility of changing, enhancing or limiting their own existence by changing their functional muscle mass. This concept is obsolete. Therefore, the pre-conceived idea that considers the efficiency of human locomotion to be solely based on the efficiency of muscle or quality of muscle continues to limit mankind as a whole. The current philosophy of human movement implies that because there are limits within muscle mass and muscle function, human locomotion is not possible from a muscle contraction. It is not the quality of man's muscle that limits or stops man's production of a task. It is movement that combines the actions of momentum and mass through the opposition to gravity that will most effectively improve man's locomotion and cognitive function. The conventional idea is that the limitation of movement is due to the gravitational pull of the earth and the percentage of a body's mass which consists of muscles. The study of mass or muscle mass function is also limited to the time in that person's life where mass supersedes the might. Within this new knowledge man must rethink the origins of movement within the mass.

# Chapter Twenty
## We are Because We Move

### *Turner's 19th theory of biological gravity*

**Any living being unable to regulate themselves within the binding gravitational force will not create typical vertical milestones without initiation, stimulation, enhancement, and the ability to breathe in equal momentum with gravitational force.**

> *"Land on Mars, a round-trip ticket - half a million dollars. It can be done."*
>
> – Elon Musk

The birthing process is fascinating and happens, or I should say needs to happen, similarly for seeds as it does for humans. Babies use compressions and interactions between the mother's active muscles creating contractions equal with her passive muscles, enabling the child to rotate, or drop into position for the birth. The act of childbirth may take hours, even days; however, true birth, or the moment of it, is when the push from the mother is met with the sudden force of gravity, creating an equal push in opposing directions as the baby's head is pushing against gravity.

As you are now seeing, this sensation happens in all directions, not just down to the ground. This is no different than a seed being stimulated as it is pushed in the ground, where the compression of the earth stimulates the roots to shoot out and the plant is equally forced in both the downward and upward direction. This gives the plant its first rotational force or movement in opposition to gravity. In both cases, life is based on movement that stems from this first interaction.

It is also significant to note that when this process is interrupted, regardless of whether it is in the plant or baby, they fail to grow and naturally rise into vertical based movements, proceeding to instead fall down.

What happens when the process is interrupted in humans? Let's look at an astronaut that has come back to Earth after a few months, potentially even a year. They can't move. Everything that you are being exposed to in this book is now reverberating through their body. They have no abilities to initiate or respond to stimuli with rotational movements. Therefore, they are unable to perform any developmental movements needed for vertical milestones or reflexes due to the fact that those are oppositional gravity-based movements. Rehabilitation is performed with immediate attention to muscle-based load/lift patterning and repeated techniques based on copying, rather than functional movements. This is arduous on the human body and allows for a slow, pain-based experience interacting with failure, defeat and anger. This is mainly due to the brain's natural reference to movement rather than interaction. In any recovery situation, noting what's wrong with a person's activity, social skills, and mobility is only compounding a situation already known to the person that you might be working with. Of course they want to move efficiently. They are well aware of complex abilities that they might have had a day, month, or year ago, yet they are unable to get back to being who they once were. They will also not attain those abilities when relying on another stable, functioning human being.

Evaluation techniques need to include the body's ability, (not necessarily the brain's) to initiate, stimulate and enhance rotational movements while opposing gravity. A baby has no cognitive reference to any movements. Therefore, in their nervous system, no movement is bad. However, not all movement equates into cognitive development. Bypassing these structures of biological gravitational responses immediately interrupts the nervous system and forces it to respond as a mass-based object or being, rather than a living organism. Until modern technology, mankind has not been able to experience these scenarios. This is one of the key reasons that autism has shifted from a genetic change to neurological responses that include movement-based issues. As humans continue to interact with cell phones as a dominant means of movement interaction, within twenty years the incidence of Alzheimer's will reach the same ratios as autism.

## *SPACE-BASED COMPLICATIONS*

The moment an astronaut enters space and goes into expansion mode, they lose all vertical milestone organizations and capabilities. They can no longer sit, stand, walk, crawl, or roll over. They lack functional movements that move through all minor and major organs. While floating is an upright position, it is not standing. Pinning one's feet or holding onto a surface is not standing. Any forms of a tether will cause immediate muscle atrophy similar to that of a trauma situation. Any apparatus applied to a human, such as an NG tube, cannulation, tracheotomy and in some cases various IV's and pulse oximeters, can cause the body to immediately atrophy. The immediate loss of bone articulation equates to the loss of the counter-response of human muscle-based responses. It's not that you need to get on the floor and grab your feet or hop on a bike and ride it. It's your brain and body's interaction that needs to know it's in an environment to do so if needed.

Current space protocols do not attend to any of these needs for prolonged human development and life-sustaining interactions. The brain/body relationship needs to be teased as if it's in an environment to produce functional movements needed for life-based tasks. Current space activities and exercises are not addressing these key factors. Notice the astronaut's use of oxygen equipment. Understand that the use of their equipment can produce atrophy even though they use it hoping to produce measurable muscle mass improvements. This practice actually causes harm to those they are trying to help.

## *SPACE-BASED ADAPTATIONS*

There are enough examples of maximum assist, spastic quadriplegics that exhibit one hundred percent muscle function however cannot run at the gravitational acceleration equated rate of 9.8 m/sec much less walk or maintain self-care. The current measurement standards of human beings' muscle function are false because they are based on the prior calculations of what is considered healthy or strong by the creator or evaluator of the initiative.

Living organisms must exhibit rotation throughout their system for all displays of force and movement. They must initiate and therefore learn from the stimulus of movement within their ability to oppose gravity. The system that cannot naturally move in and out of rotation is guaranteed to fail to exhibit the controlled cognitive movements as in sitting, crawling and jumping or other deemed measurements of force.

Space movement programs need to change to include all of these principles into daily operational interaction.

Astronauts exhibit a decrease in or lack of peripheral vision. These same movement/vision issues occur in those with autism or Alzheimer's.

Our ability to visually work the room counteracts with the sweeping or peripheral movements needed in the coccyx. Any action needed for pronation needs to be developed with special tailbone interaction. This opposition of force is not able to naturally exhibit in outer space. In all three categories, the eyes align with head movements, removing the body's ability or need for crossing midline. This leads to a rapid regression in neuro-mapping needed for simple tasks such as in reading and writing, as well as short-term and long-term memory skills. Going through the motions and getting from point A to point B is not how the brain is wired for progressive and medium-level to high-level movement patterns. Inner organ complications from constipation, breathing and digestive interaction are the first signs of the body's breakdown or aging process. Astronauts are put through grueling rehabilitation after long-term missions in space and are studied down to a cellular level. Changing the space habitation and performing skills that are completely new to the human brain and body's core movements can help to reduce rehabilitative complexities upon their return. An astronaut cannot go around performing tasks with their feet clamped or attached to the floor. This is no different than placing a child or adult in orthotics expecting heel-to-toe gait with peripheral visual field interaction. In both cases, there is also a halt of the body's ability to perform visual arching. The loss of the milestone of coming to sitting equally impacts one's performance or response of a visual arch. For an astronaut, what was once an inner core movement is now an external sensation from outside the body. No longer is their movement stemming from the pelvis or base of the feet. In space, an officer develops a new movement structure through the top of the feet as the momentum of a touch opposition to movement rather than the lower extremities processing against the upper extremities for oppositional force with rotation.

# Chapter Twenty One

# Movement Cognition

## *Turner's 20th theory of biological gravity*

**A living being that is unable to create equal responses in passive and active muscle-based and force-based applications, is the same as a person with no concerns for its relationship to life forces.**

> *"I believe a leaf of grass is no less than the journey-work of the stars."*
>
> – Walt Whitman

I really hope when you are reading this, walking around the house or going about your daily routine, you are not asking yourself if you are breathing. At the same time, you cannot think about getting up when your body wants to sit down. Are you grunting and groaning through transitional skills, while your body's internal processes become dominated by the force of gravity? If you are, your system is not only failing within its movement vocabulary, it is also unable to learn and process successful actions. The mind has switched to preventative behaviors.

In space, the longer the duration, the more natural law diminishes from the human body. An astronaut already knows they can't be a couch potato. The second they leave Earth's binding force, the muscular deviations for strength, endurance and range of motion (ROM) come into play. ROM is not a functional movement and will never be able to produce a transitional, functional, or milestone movement. It is not a term used in my work at Movement Lesson™ as it is not an approach to development. It is a measure of range and that is all it is. One of the best exercises in regard to passive/active muscle and force-based actions are in the degrees of our push/pull milestones as seen in tug-o-war or riding a bicycle.

Key primitive stresses are needed throughout our lives. The passive response always wants to be the most dominant in emotions as well as our physical traits. Even our 'progress' in equalizing the training of men and women has resulted in more uniform movements and thereby severely changed necessary physiological approaches. This needs to be noted in the ISS training program in particular. In space, you don't want the hot shot next to you when your life is depending on survival within the next few minutes. You're also playing with some big toys in outer space. There is no time for a Friday night joy ride with some free-range spacewalks or extravehicular activity.

The key dynamics needed for short-term and long-term space travel are being overlooked. We naturally have push/pull dynamics within the layers of our skin and gravity. Similar to the Earth's atmosphere, as in its orbits, space bends or pushes around the planet as an active force-based application. Just like climbing in and out of bed, daily tasks in space act in a similar manner as gravity manipulates our body. Obviously, it does this more efficiently and optimally as it experiences this through rotational movements. When a body cannot create these actions and responses, death creeps into view.

During a natural delivery, in the contraction phase, a mother's womb is delivering, or I should say, transferring, very specific movements needed to organize for opposing the gravitational force that is about to hit the baby's nervous system. This is the crucial active and passive phase needed for all future muscle-based responses. This is not to be confused with muscle-based movements. We are all familiar with contractions, as the womb is ejecting the baby from its comfortable home. However, the true physiological significance of this period is to transfer specific movement vocabulary from the mature system to the immature system.

During the womb period, all of the natural principles of gravity presented here are not available or achievable. It is neurologically significant because the astronauts experience this neuro-switch in outer space immediately when they experience what is considered weightlessness. In actuality, it is expansion mode. In the womb, the body was not meant to experience friction, force or gravity as we know it. The fetus is able to expand in all directions to form all organs, in a micro-cellular level to develop in unison. This same bio-system kicks in during space travel, posing the greatest threat to the human's biological systems and functions. This is why many of the space-based responses need to be redirected to minimize the 'engagement' of expansion mode.

It is the contractions that offer the presenting baby the first force of opposition. This period still doesn't include rotational movements.

This force is specific to initiate a movement-based response, not muscle-based response. I repeat, this is not to stimulate a muscle-based but a movement-based response.

A human being does not have a specific cognitive response for a reason. We are meant to organize first with movement. These movements are all organized around the force of gravity. It is within these key moments that are some of the greatest determining factors that may define the rest of our life. These forces need to be organized prior to the body and brain's ability to respond in any cognitive organization. Therefore, all cognitive responses need to have these movements as precedence. It is within these first movement responses the body's system mechanics need to be initiated and stimulated in its priority.

The contractions place the first organized force on the baby's systems. Equally effective, at the same time, are the mother's passive muscles that allow the baby to turn into a downward position to be presented for the birthing process or in actuality the presenting to gravity process. The mother's floor and pelvic dilation open to a position for her force to be less than gravity's force for the baby to leave her system.

Another crucial observation of this phase is that the system is not just being forced, the system is responding to a force to create movements. This is where living beings differ from Newton's observation for equal and opposition forces. It is true that I am capable of opposing a force from you or an inanimate object with an equal response. However, in most cases, neuro-typical responses are based on counterbalance rather than counter-oppositional movements. Which can be changed and manipulated based on the body's cognitive and gravitational responses that can change equally for counterbalance or unequally to submissive responses. Calculations are also needed for inner-cellular responses to mass, rotation and buoyancy that include cellular and systemic dynamics. Movements are not muscle-based. Muscle responds to movement; that includes contractions, based on the neurological, cognitive and systemic responses, that may also include emotional and social interactions depending on age, development and ability to respond to all of the above. The more we are able to move in opposition to gravity with rotational movements, the more we are able to develop.

A baby during the birthing process, if they responded as Newton observed, would perish upon birth. Similar to escaping velocity, the reasoning for all my research, the rotation/momentum needed to escape gravity for inanimate objects has a direct and severely direct correlation for all of life's existence. A human being's first key rotational movements, similar to a rocket launch, responds to the force, not with equal force, but rotational interaction opposing the observation of an equal downward force. This is why it's so important to understand that any baby that is unable to respond to stimuli with rotational movements is guaranteed to require assistance or is special needs. This interaction with gravity is a natural phenomenon that is in your body at this very moment. Equally, it is unable to present in outer space. It is within these movement dynamics that the space program must change the metrics to determine how an astronaut manipulates these crucial movement responses and is then able to adjust to include them during their time in outer space.

It's really funny to see simple explanations of Newton's *Law of Motion* shown with two human beings pushing against each other with ice skates on. Science's version of friction is funny since those observations rarely occur in nature. I would really like to see two rams going at it with ice skates on. The conferred metrics of passive and active muscle interaction takes on a whole new perspective.

The propulsion of a baby from the mother systematically initiates opposition of gravity, rotational and buoyancy responses through the body's system mechanics, organ and cellular expansion process as similarly seen in an observation of a type of breathing. Similar to what we can visually see with the ebbing and flowing of tides, humans, the Earth and other living units need to 'breathe', or expand and release, not necessarily contract, within their processes of interaction with other living units. This is another key to the workings of the force of gravity in larger systems as we see in a solar system. Remember, however, we do not see this action on a non-living being, as with the Moon, or a rock. This is why I continue to caution on long-term colonization of the lunar surface. Our body's relationship and responses to exercise need to be different for lunar habitation than a space station or planet-based habitation. This is also why we cannot introduce centrifugal force to any man or organization based living unit! The changes to a man's body at a microscopic level would be too fast and, in most cases, unable to be redirected for optimal long-term life responses. The brain and body would deteriorate in proportional amounts. Water and food are needed to live; so is breathing. We cannot habitate an environment which is unable to equally breathe. In addition to Newton's observation "To every action there is always opposed an equal reaction: or the mutual actions of two bodies upon each other are always equal and directed to contrary parts."[17] This

17 This translation of the third law and the commentary following it can be found in the "Principia" on page 20 of volume 1 of the 1729 translation

noted opposition can only be done through beings that have the ability to manipulate opposition of gravity and force with the use of buoyancy and rotational movements.

How would I lessen the power of someone who is going to hit me? A fist comes at you, even if you are unresponsive, Newton's Law really can't come into play. Why? Because even at a cellular level, your body will be responding with these principles. Depending on where you are with these principles, is how your body changes power through movement.

A child with cerebral palsy is having a startle due to the fact that they have a very low to non-responsive rotational representation, an equally low buoyancy rate that increases the gravitational force negative to opposing gravity because of the extreme high of hyperactive muscle-based for non-transitional skills. Equally, a person with very low ability or inability to present with a reflex could also have an equally low or non-rotational response and low to non-buoyancy response with hyper-passive muscle-based for non-transitional skills. Therefore, with astronauts, it's important to present changes in the body's responsive outcomes and not continue with load/lift variations because we are not going to get long-term muscular gains by focusing on a visual concern of muscle atrophy. The matrix for functional movements has changed past the dynamics of the brain's ability to use the movement for neurological information. This is the breaking point and lapse to the cognitive, social/emotional inter-changes for transitional developmental movement patterns. Just changing the momentum responses will equally change all of our internal and external processors within all the information that I'm presenting. This is where we can add into the equation the body's interaction with not only drugs and alcohol but with food.

Many of us believe that muscle functions are based on the contraction of muscles. However, in reality they interact with the forces and functions of the body's response to the forces that interact with gravity. This interaction must be in opposition of gravity. All of human development, neuro-cognitive skills, aging, and disease/mitochondrial interaction depends on this relationship. It's the key to life as we know it.

## *SPACE-BASED COMPLICATIONS*

Space-based complications are just not allowed on the International Space Station. Any pilot and crew practice countless routines for performance and task preparation and organization, for the routine daily projects, to those never needed due to their diligence and skills. Recognizing the observations for our human biologies needed for, not only the survival, but the evolution, must take place this very hour. Not having the movement equipment, similar to the body response found in calisthenics application, for the micro cellular responses will destroy any hope of occupying Mars and any other rock in space.

Imagine never doing a jumping jack. Gross muscle load without the interaction of passive/active inner-muscular responses will not carry the body. The lack of gravity or the float cognitively changes the movements into passive responses. The interior skeletal needs for counterbalance are now gone due to the lack of space agency preparedness. The longer this prevails, the more the life force diminishes in the body. This point is brought home by the continued pre-space compilation of efforts to recreate drills underwater. Noticing the similarities of the two should be the first clue to changes needed for our beloved efforts in space. Since we can't live underwater for a day, why would we create a learning environment that our biology knows is deadly? We can all agree the movement responses are similar to outer space. Then why do it? The correct approach to space travel needs to include all aspects of bodily changes for cellular construction in skeletal, muscular, and circulatory principles for the immediate deviations in passive and active neuro-muscular life based forces.

This is similar to the problem seen in Spinal Muscular Atrophy (SMA) type 1. This is a muscular dystrophy that can present at birth and is often only detectable by my Newborn Movement Assessment, the interior presentation is this book in reverse. Unfortunately, many rare genetics go undetected at birth and the baby goes home from the hospital with the hope that the pediatrician will catch the condition and test the child. On the flip-side, no parent is monitoring their child for aggressive regression. In short, the inner muscle rotation within the sarcomere continues on a progress path of development from birth. However, once the muscles stop their synchronized inner rotational movements the myosin/actin relationship ends. Various conditions from environmental, trauma, and/or neurological complications; as seen in the neuromuscular breakdown in a baby presenting with SMA1 include the loss of passive and active muscle and force based application, down to the sucking and breathing, and the child is therefore starting to pass away. This is also the cause of our demise in aging and now a true relation to this twentieth biological gravitational reaction of a living being, unable to create equal responses in passive and active muscle and force based applications, is the same as a person with no concerns for its relationship to life forces.

## *SPACE-BASED ADAPTATIONS*

This is a crucial natural principle. Although I've presented it last, it needs to be as significant as the first. It's one of the first applications for changes needed for pre-flight and during flight time to maintain all human, biological functions. The duration of time in the ISS is in a non-gravitational environment. This is the most harmful to the body vs the planetary time we are used to experiencing. Establishing these natural principles from within can help anyone and everybody. It's our essential to life and breakdown from life. From assessing infants at birth to the officer pre to post flight, evaluations can and need to be established for optimal long-term gains. It's not about the strength of the muscle but the health response and ability to be responsive to transition in and out of positions for function. All adaptive equipment needs to be designed to incorporate equal responses in passive and active muscle and force based applications.

The development of living beings is based on their ability to respond to stimuli; it initiates and develops cognitive functions. It is only after millions of movement variations that include rotation, mass and acceleration that brain function is at a level to manipulate its environment on a repetitive basis. The epidermis functions as a constant for the external force of gravity, per square inch, around the body. Thus creating a constant imprint of gravity itself. Although it is true that a body can fall down at the same rate of speed as an apple, the apple has not the ability to get up again. An adult human could come up with a thousand examples of how to get up based on their life experiences, mass and rotation. The activation of a hormone related to the hypothalamus or nerve impulses that activate muscle function will not and can not get a man off the floor. However, if there is damage to either of those system functions, it is true that man's ability to rise will be compromised. Realize that genetics, a trauma, or damage to the body can equally affect movement calculations, as does the use of gravity.

# Chapter Twenty Two
## A Forced Attraction

### *Turner's 21st theory of biological gravity*

**A living being manipulates the lower binding force of gravity to catapult movement from above and thereby creates inner momentum. On the contrary, inanimate objects may become a pendulum; interacting with both the Earth's gravity and rotation in isolated momentum as a constant.**

> *"I think humans will reach Mars, and I would like to see it happen in my lifetime."*
>
> – Buzz Aldrin

Marcas Chown, author of The Ascent of Gravity, states that gravity is actually a very weak force. You and I, when we stick our arm and hand out to the side at shoulder level, are able to oppose gravity with very little effort. However, this action is not a functional movement. Holding your arm out is a static action because there is not one thing in this pose that is needed to stay alive. It may be true gravity is so weak that I can lift my hand and hold it out to the side. However, a person can't feed or dress themself in this pose. When the body performs or is unable to move in and out between a functional and a non-functional movement, the muscle structure becomes abnormal and emits hypo and hypertonic responses. This is one of the primary reasons for muscle atrophy complications that are associated with space travel. However, it is the momentum in movement that is needed for the achievement and administration of strength guided within the muscle for function.

Whether you play ball or not, we can all imagine the planting of the opposing foot as the pitcher raises their arm to take hold of the anchor in an attempt to catapult the ball towards the batter. Imagine holding a pair of chopsticks, held together by a rubber band creating a slingshot. Now you're holding the bottom of the chopsticks and pulling back on the top part and suddenly flinging a cherry across the room. The anchor of gravity below gives me the momentum of the band on top. No different for a child exploring going to all fours as they start to bounce before they crawl. In the lack of infant development professionals can notice a child's inability to manipulate or create momentum during early stages of development rather than ponder whether they are really deviating in milestones. Within this crucial and early manipulation of natural force is also one of the most overlooked or misunderstood aspects of typical to atypical progression. From rolling over, feeding, any vertical milestones, to just opening something, vestibular bending of momentum will offer success in almost every toddler task.

Noting the previous theories, anybody, unable to produce and manipulate gravity will be unable to transition into the bending of gravity. Nasa Astronaut Bob Behnken was unable to bend gravity while exiting the Dragon spacecraft to greet fellow crew members of the ISS. To compensate, he needed to hold onto a bar and pull to outstretch his hand in thanks. Some very basic push/pull milestones are unachievable in outer space as it would be with a special child unable to develop their primary social skills. During the same period, nothing comes into the conscious mind until we have comparison. Babies then go into the process of oppositional gravity with rotational responses to the manipulation transitional skills to those of achievement with purposeful movement. This is why infant developmental movement patterns need to be explored through weight transfer rather than specific muscle-based actions.

The human body is unable to create an axis or reference point to movements. Approximations can be delivered; however, the actual manipulation of the task is an image, only to be manipulated by the user's past experiences and calculations. One of the important aspects of lying, in both prone and supine, is when a baby moves against various anchors around their bodies; even when unable to touch the floor. This is where living beings can be incredible as they are able to move through the air. Michael Jordan can create complexities as he levitates or walks his pelvis through the air, is still able to bend gravity, and slams the basketball in. The development of these skills is endless, and they are also absent in outer space. It all starts as a baby is being vaginally born and their skull bones go against and through gravity. From there, the baby is lying on their belly as their head and body moves in space. Then the cornea of the eye finds gravity as the back of the eye counters against gravity. The directional movements bend and create momentum responses from within. Whereas, the Foucault pendulum is capable of demonstrating Earth's rotation only due to the suspension of mass above gravity. If it was able to succumb to gravity, the mass couldn't articulate the isolation momentum as a constant.

## *SPACE-BASED COMPLICATIONS*

You and I can still move in outer space. However, due to our bodies' inability to respond within these movement features, we are left with the lack of moments of comparison needed for manipulation. If we were to put a baby into outer space, without these tools that nature has provided us, they would resemble little water bubbles floating around the station.

When we need to stand after surgery, we can blame the buckling of a leg on a lack of muscle tone, but it is still our relationship to gravity and lack of rotational movements. The recovery from an injury or disability using braces to hold a leg or body into position is not the answer, as it takes away the remaining hopes of nature's ability to initiate the needed responses. During this period, you cannot make someone strong enough to overcome their ability to oppose nature and mass. It has to be the relationship of gravity in the nervous system to produce functional movements

Another key difference on Earth is man's structure involved to create the needed task.

All of this knowledge forms the basis for every client evaluation I perform. It affects everything from how I look at hip x-rays to evaluating vision, because the structure itself is going to affect the relationship with gravity's interaction for functional movement. Just as a living being might look like he is coming to the floor but is not succumbing to gravity. A football player dives in the end zone to complete the touchdown in a momentous roll and is right back up into his victory jump. Generally, a plant has no interest in sleep or lying down, a pea plant starts off in a moment and is headed for, we say, the sun and air via water. Looking at the plant's life through oppositional gravity with rotation, that's what allows that plant to grow. Without this interaction the plant will just die. This is why trees don't fall down. This is why we don't fall down. Observing a young toddler, they do not fall down. They might fall off of things, but they are not suddenly walking and then just fall down. However, this is what my son did after he got sick during key developmental stages.

It is within this twenty-first theory that we learn not to study and work with weakness in the body, we go after strength. And that's where the misconception is, to go after muscles, assuming muscles equate to strength.

## *SPACE-BASED ADAPTATIONS*

A mature movement uses gravity as an anchor rather than a reactive pinning force. Your body is able to use this natural force in 360 degrees for a momentous strength. This is why I like karate so much; because I have to hit you with my left hand just as much as my right hand. Now, I know I hit better with my right. But if you were attacking me from my left, I have to be equally prepared. When I took up karate, I wasn't looking for a fight. I just liked the fact that every part of your body needed to participate.

First, as babies, our bodies get hit with momentum, anchoring a position against a vertical opposition to gravity. Then we respond with momentum by taking a toy past midline with rotational movements. From there, we can manipulate it, going into push/pull milestones to load/lift as we explore our new environments. In space, we have no momentum: we hit or touch something and it repels the body. Even a water droplet can move away rather than interact. An anchor is now a hook or a tether, replacing or preventing the opposing movements from happening. Changing our neurological representation of all internal responses and spatial depth perceptions. There is no rotational response, so an astronaut now has to move onto push/pull milestones as the means of horizontal transportation with no load/lift calculations in sight. The human dynamics are completely altered.

Why do babies not have a hand preference? All these features of natural law must be neutral. In outer space they are all calculated. A baby just responds to stimuli. To do this they have to oppose gravity with rotational movement. It has always been that simple. There's no good touch, there's no bad touch. I say that and teach that all the time. In our formation, there are no good movements, and no bad movements. Those movements or responses change when a parent's notion of right and wrong or correct behavior or movements come into play. Redirecting their actions or changing the environment. It is these interactions, simple yet life-changing, that can be very detrimental to a child's short-term and long-term future. This is the basis of my work at my Movement Lesson™ clinic as I work with children and adults who were told they wouldn't be able to achieve a myriad of milestones and activities. During crucial first years of my son's development, he was informed he would never walk or talk. His changes created my changes. A vast difference of a parent to child versus a child to parent.

In this equation of gravity - rotation and buoyancy are the keys to understanding why muscles don't create movement, they respond to the interaction of it. We do need a type of strength but not how science currently views muscle mass organization. That is an easy number to look at but that's not where strength comes from - it's just a measurable unit. This is also where many traditional therapies can fail us due to looking at external manipulations. This is an example of why trying harder won't help. It will make matters worse with a child's processing powers within movement. A body's attempt to try or mimic takes properties away from other necessary life skills - like do not fall - so the brain goes back to those tasks as if they never had skills to begin with due to cognitive only force-based manipulations.

Moving forward, the efforts of science to understand and implement these principles, as they relate to everyone from babies to astronauts, is critical to changing the interaction of inner based core movements to determine and influence counterbalance and rotational interactions in opposition to gravity. **The entire future of our efforts in space depends on getting this right.**

*THIS IS YOUR SPACE MANUAL!*

# Chapter Twenty Three

## You Can't Get To Mars Without Me

We have wanted to get off this rock for a long time. The need for exploration has been in our bones for centuries. As we move into a more modern time of the cell phone, stories of our evolutions through movements have been forgotten. The power of a rocket is the only thing left that makes us look out and up. I don't know of many people who would pass up a chance to see a rocket launch, have lunch with Elon Musk or spend the day at the Museum of Cosmonautics. (The last time I was there I noted that it's closed on Monday, so I was unable to visit. Maybe I will be able to lecture there in the future.) At the very same time, many are quick to point out that our efforts and finances are useless because we can't live in outer space. At the very same moment, we have babies that won't be able to go to outer space because they are unable to entertain the binding forces of gravity as it has been presented to all of us. Questions relating to gravity have just changed because you've read this book. You can no longer question the tools needed for the future of mankind's evolution.

All your life you were told gravity does exist with no explanation. For the longest time it was a falling force, then a pinning force, and then a wave. Science and research have deemed gravity to be the weakest of all basic forces. A natural force where our feet are happy to play but are equally happy doing a Chuck Norris thrust kick without falling to the floor. We can finally walk away from that darn apple to the planets above if we take all these biological features and use them in outer space. This is meant to be a light read to redirect your thoughts and research into a new science of rotational mathematics. Degrees and studies will open up with new fields and fellowships to produce the equations needed to complete the mission.

I have spent years trying and helping all of us move better. It is my mission to eradicate special needs, other than genetics, from this planet. Wonderful, smart people are unable to engage and grasp these 21 simple yet profound natural principles.

Imagine being told your baby might get it, your son is too uncoordinated to make the team, Harvard is a dream because of your daughter's complex inabilities with rotational midlines. All of these statements are true.

Not only can you not get to Mars without me, new fields of biological and movement sciences need to be created and developed. I took a moment to look outside what I was being told. I have worked with so many people struggling to move, but it wasn't muscle-based or worse, muscle memory. I have a lot more to tell you about gravity, movement, buoyancy, momentum, where we are in space and where we are going.

Whether you are more familiar with mass, the small particles in quantum physics or have been pondering with general relativity, this shines a new light, or I should say a new movement, into all areas of the binding force. We are no longer associating the three forces of electromagnetism, the weak and strong force, but look to gravity, not quantum gravity, with rotation, buoyancy and momentum as equal partners in crime. Gravity isn't from a distant future or past; it is right before us and we are able to walk through it and interact with it as part of our structure for foundational movements. The way you move is because you were the baby who responded to opposing gravity. To do so, like the space shuttle, you needed to respond with rotational movements. I hope I can continue to teach you how to get to space, because you can't get to Mars without me.